ABIGAIL ADAMS

The President's Lady

Abigail Adams:

ILLUSTRATED BY ROBERT FRANKENBERG

The President's Lady

REGINA Z. KELLY

HOUGHTON MIFFLIN COMPANY · BOSTON

NEW YORK · ATLANTA · GENEVA, ILL. · DALLAS · PALO ALTO

Contents

Library of Congress Catalog Card No. 62–9303

B
Adec
april

CHAPTER 1

Fire!

With her parents, Abigail Smith stood at the door of the meeting house in Weymouth. She and her older sister Mary curtseyed as their father, Reverend William Smith, greeted those who came for the Sunday service. Five-year-old Will, like his father, bowed and held out his hand.

The Simpson family was the last to arrive. "I'm sorry we're late, Reverend," said Mr. Simpson, who was one of the richest sheep raisers in Massachusetts. "But I was shearing until after sundown yesterday and overslept."

"And I have such a bad cold," added Mrs. Simpson.

"Then I'm glad you brought your foot warmer," said Abigail's mother, pointing to the square iron box filled with hot coals which

Mr. Simpson carried by a handle. "It's still cold in the meeting house, even though it is so late in April."

"Make your curtsey now, Hannah," said Mrs. Simpson, nudging her ten-year-old daughter.

Then they all went indoors, the minister last of all.

Abigail's eyes wandered while her father preached. She was seven years old and wanted to pay attention, but it was hard at times to understand his sermon. In the next pew, she saw Mr. Simpson nod a little.

"He must be tired from the sheepshearing," thought Abigail.

Mrs. Simpson put a spray of caraway into her husband's hand. Nibbling the seeds sometimes kept one awake.

James Trowbridge, the tithing man, walked up the aisle, his head busily turning from side to side. In his hand was a long stick called a tithing rod. It had a round brass knob at one end.

Mr. Simpson leaned back and rested his

head in a corner of the pew. Slowly he began
to slip down, a little at a time. Mrs. Simpson,
with her eyes closed, was still sitting firmly
erect in her seat, but she also began to nod.

Abigail's eyes widened. The tithing man
had drawn near. His long pole with the brass
knob was held tightly in his hand.

Whack!

The stick came down, and the knob hit
Mr. Simpson squarely on the head.

Red-faced and sleepy-eyed, he jumped to his feet. He seized his wife by the shoulders and began to shake her violently. "Stand still, will ye!" he yelled.

"Henry! I'm your wife! Not a sheep!" Mrs. Simpson cried, holding tightly to her bonnet. "Wake up! Let me go!"

There was soft laughter all around them.

"Mr. Simpson must be dreaming that he's shearing sheep," thought Abigail, trying hard not to giggle.

Reverend Smith stopped his sermon. But Abigail thought she saw a twinkle in her father's eye.

Everyone stretched to see. The meeting house was noisy with the sound of banging seats and shuffling feet. The small boys on the pulpit stairway pushed and shoved each other, knowing that the tithing man was too busy to stop them. One almost tumbled from the top step.

"We will now have the baptism of the children who were born this week," Reverend Smith announced loudly.

10

"Henry! How you have shamed me!" Mrs. Simpson cried.

With one hand, she grasped Hannah's hand. With the other, she pushed her red-faced husband out of their pew. As Mrs. Simpson swept from the pew, Abigail thought she heard something clatter on the floor.

Outside, after the service was over, Hannah Simpson ran to meet Abigail.

"My father says he's going to punch the tithing man on the nose," said Hannah excitedly. "He hit him hard on purpose because my father caught him cheating when we had our wool weighed last week."

Mr. Trowbridge, the tithing man, was the wool buyer for Weymouth.

"Come, Hannah. Your father has the wagon ready," Mrs. Simpson called.

A little later, from a window of the parsonage, which was near the meeting house, Abigail watched the few remaining people leave. The last to go were her father and Deacon Brown. Then she heard the roll of a wagon coming toward the meeting house.

She wondered a little, for on the Lord's Day, no one came to visit unless the parson was called for sudden illness.

She saw Mr. Simpson get out of the wagon and go into the meeting house. Could he be looking for the tithing man? In a few minutes, Mr. Simpson came out and turned into a nearby lane. This led to the house where Mr. Trowbridge lived.

"Maybe Mr. Simpson is going to punch Mr. Trowbridge on the nose," thought Abigail hopefully. But he couldn't do that on the Lord's Day, she decided regretfully.

"Abigail, it's time to eat supper," Mrs. Smith called.

Abigail opened the window and peered toward the lane. But there was no sign of Mr. Simpson.

"We'll go to bed early," said Mrs. Smith after supper and evening prayers were over. "It's been a long day."

Later, in bed, Abigail blinked her eyes and looked at the window of her little attic room. It was bright with light. The sun couldn't have risen already!

She shook Mary, who shared her bed and who had not stirred. "Wake up! It's late," said Abigail. Why hadn't their mother called them?

Then she looked at the window again. *The light was flickering!* There were loud crackling sounds outside. A woman screamed. Somewhere below, a man shouted, "Parson Smith! The fire is spreading!"

Then Abigail heard her father running up the steep, narrow stairs. "Abigail! Mary! Wake up! The meeting house is on fire. The parsonage may go next!" he was shouting.

Abigail scrambled from the bed. The parsonage was their own house!

Reverend Smith was in the room now and pulling the blankets from the bed. "Put on your shoes," he cried. "You have no time to dress. Wrap yourselves in the blankets.

13

The sparks may fall on the roof any minute!"

"Did you wake up Will?" asked Abigail, tugging on her shoes. Her fingers were clumsy with the laces as she hurried.

"He was the first to see the fire. He woke us up," said Parson Smith as he wrapped a blanket around Abigail. "Your mother has Betsey."

"Hurry, Mary," said Abigail. "Here are your shoes."

But Mary was screaming wildly and holding on to the bedpost. She was ten, nearly three years older than Abigail, but more easily frightened.

"Put on your shoes, Mary!" her father commanded. "We've no time to lose."

Mary only screamed louder and did not move.

"I'll put them on for her!" cried Abigail, who had at last managed to tie the ribbons of her own shoes. Her heart was pounding, but she knew that Mary was helpless with fear. In a minute, Abigail was tugging at one of her sister's shoes.

14

"My brave little lass!" said Parson Smith, giving Abigail a quick pat. He knelt and put on Mary's other shoe.

"William! William!" Mrs. Smith called from below. "Come quickly! The flames are beginning to rise to the steeple!"

15

"The town gunpowder is stored in the steeple!" the parson cried. "It may blow up any minute! Run, Abigail!" He pushed her ahead of him down the steep stairs. Mary was limp in his arms and moaning softly.

Outside, men were forming in a line to the parsonage, passing leather buckets filled with water from the well.

"No use trying to save the meeting house, Reverend," called one. "We'll wet down your house, if we can."

"Get back, everyone! Get back!" the parson shouted. "The gunpowder is in the steeple! It may blow up any minute!"

At once, everyone rushed away from the meeting house. Will gave a helping hand to his mother, who was carrying the baby. Abigail clung to her father's long cloak. He still carried Mary in his arms.

Suddenly, there was a deafening blast. The whole sky was red with light. Pieces of flaming wood flew in all directions. Big sparks came down like fiery rain.

Abigail tumbled over the root of a tree

16

and fell flat and hard. The red whirled
around her and grew black. Then she saw
nothing.

When she opened her eyes again, the glowing light in the sky had dimmed. There
were thick clouds of slowly moving smoke.

The crackling noises were coming to an end.

"It's all over, Abigail. The meeting house has burned to the ground," she heard her father say sadly. Covered with her father's big black cloak, she was lying at the foot of a tree. The cloak smelled of smoke and burned wool.

"Is the parsonage burned?" Abigail thought her voice sounded very far away.

"Just a little part of the roof," said her mother. She was seated on the ground with her arms around Mary, who was sobbing now and then, but was otherwise quiet.

"The men saved our house with their water buckets," said Parson Smith.

"We should go to the house now, William," said his wife. "We must make a good breakfast for all our friends."

"Come, Mary," said her father firmly. "Get up now and walk." He turned to Abigail. "Can you walk by yourself?"

But Abigail was already on her feet and trying to fold her father's long cloak. Mary began to cry.

"I'll hold your hand, Mary," said Abigail. Together, they walked toward the house.

Some of the men who had helped put out the fire walked with them.

"How do you suppose the fire started, Reverend?" asked Henry Simpson.

"A spark, perhaps, from someone's foot warmer at the service yesterday," said Parson Smith. "It's been very dry, you know, and the timber in the meeting house was old."

"There were no foot warmers used at the service," said Mr. Simpson. "Except —" Then he stopped.

Abigail stared. She was remembering what she had seen yesterday. Mr. Simpson hadn't carried his foot warmer when his wife had hurried him from his pew after the service. Abigail was sure he didn't have it in his hand when he had come out of the meeting house the second time. But he had just told her father that no one had had a foot warmer at the service.

"Except —"

CHAPTER 2

Who Is to Blame?

"You may read your Bible in your father's study," said Mrs. Smith to Abigail later in the morning. "He will be busy checking on the damage."

Abigail liked to be in her father's study. The shelves were filled with books. Often her father let her look at the books and spell out some of the words. She really could not read the chapter in the Bible, but she had heard it so often that she could guess at most of the words.

Reverend Smith had begun teaching Abigail her letters and numbers when she was four.

"Abigail is too delicate to walk the two miles across the fields to the Dame's School," Mrs. Smith had said.

"Then I'll teach her at home," Reverend Smith had decided.

At first he used the hornbook, which was made up of pages from the New England Primer covered with thin, clear sheets of horn. In less than a year, Abigail could read parts of the Catechism and some of the hymns in the Bay Psalm Book.

"She is the smartest child in Weymouth," Reverend Smith told his wife.

"It's time for dinner," Mrs. Smith called to Abigail at noon. "Your father is here, and I have maple sugar for the corn pudding."

Abigail waited impatiently while prayers were said and her father served the corn pudding. It was always the first course in all New England households. She hurriedly scraped her bowl, so that she could talk while her father carved the chicken.

"Hannah Simpson told me yesterday that her father was going to punch Mr. Trowbridge on the nose," she said importantly. "Mr. Simpson caught him cheating with the wool weight, and Hannah said that's why the tithing man hit her father so hard in the meeting house."

Reverend Smith put down his carving knife and shook his head in reproof. "You should not speak evil of anyone, Daughter," he said. "Even if you know evil to be true, you should not repeat it."

Abigail blushed and bent over her plate. She was ashamed now that she had gossiped. Her father had told her before that she should not repeat evil.

For the rest of the meal, she kept quiet while her parents talked about the fire.

"The meeting house is completely destroyed," said Reverend Smith. "Even our communion serving pieces are melted."

"I wonder how it started," said Mrs. Smith.

"No one knows," answered her husband. "The blaze was high before Will woke us."

Abigail started to speak, then almost bit her tongue. She had meant to tell her father that she had seen Mr. Simpson come out of the meeting house a second time after every-

23

one had left. "Maybe he had something to do with starting the fire," thought Abigail. "But I'm not sure."

Her father had just told her not to repeat evil stories even if they were true. She could not bear to have him reprove her again. It was better to say nothing.

The sun was bright on the following Sunday, and so the meeting was held outdoors near the parsonage. All during the week, Deacon Brown had been visiting the members of the congregation. The meeting house was to be rebuilt at once. Each man was to contribute lumber, nails, and labor according to how much he could afford.

"We'll have the roof-raising on Wednesday, if it's a good day," announced the Deacon after the morning service.

Everybody was expected to help put up the framework of the building. The women would bring food, and there would be a feast and pleasant gathering after the work was done.

24

"I'll give an extra keg of nails," promised Mr. Simpson.

Abigail had been watching him all morning. What had he been doing in the meeting house after everyone had left? A dozen times that week, she had asked herself that question. But she had said nothing about this to her father. She did not want to be told again that she should not repeat evil. But what had Mr. Simpson been doing in the meeting house?

The Smiths ate with the rest of the congregation. Everyone talked about the fire and wondered how it had started.

"It's been so dry this year, the least spark could start a fire," said Parson Smith.

"I have my own views on the matter, and I have written them down in verse," said Paul Torrey.

He was the schoolmaster, and he prided himself on the ease with which he could write rhymes.

"What are they, man?" asked the minister.

Paul Torrey piled his plate high with food

25

from the Simpsons' basket. He boarded with the various families during the school term, and he knew that the Simpsons served fine meals.

"I'll post my verses now," said the schoolmaster, tacking a long piece of paper on a wall of the parsonage. Everyone crowded around to see as Parson Smith read the verses aloud.

> Our powder stock, kept under lock
> With flints and bullets were
> By dismal blast soon swiftly cast
> Into the open air.
>
> I'm satisfied, the culprits live
> Somewhere within the town.
> Therefore, no doubt, you'll find them out
> By searching up and down.
>
> On trial then we will condemn
> The sentence we will give.
> Them execute without dispute,
> Not being fit to live.

The Parson turned toward the schoolmaster. "It is your duty, Mr. Torrey, to tell

us the name of the person you suspect," he demanded, "but not unless you are sure," he added sharply. "What proof do you have?"

"I have means of knowing," said the schoolmaster, looking mysterious. "I was around until long after the baptizing."

The Parson reread:

> Them execute without dispute,
> Not being fit to live.

He frowned at the schoolmaster. "Do you really believe a man should have his life taken for such a deed, or were you just looking for a word to rhyme?" he asked.

The schoolmaster flushed. "Aye. The rhyme was hard, I confess. But I have good reasons for my suspicions."

"Did you see anyone go in or near the meeting house after the service?" the Parson asked.

Abigail stared at Mr. Simpson. Would he tell that he had gone into the meeting house after everyone had left?

28

But Simpson had already pushed to the front of the little crowd. "I was the last in the meeting house that day, Parson," he said. "I went back to look for our foot warmer. I'd forgotten it."

His face grew a little red as the people laughed.

"That's right, Reverend." The tithing man had come forward. "Simpson came to my house later for his foot warmer. I had picked it up for him after the service. I knew it was my fault that it had been forgotten."

"But how did you know Mr. Trowbridge had your foot warmer?" the Parson asked Mr. Simpson.

"I didn't until I went to his house," he replied. "We had had an argument over the weight of my wool. I found out that I had made a mistake, and I wanted to tell him so."

"Well, it is good to have at least two honest, forgiving men among us," said the Parson. For a second, he turned to look at

Abigail, but she hung her head. Her cheeks were warm with her shame. Her father had been right to tell her never to repeat evil.

The Parson looked sternly at the schoolmaster. "Do you now think you know who caused the fire?" asked Reverend Smith.

The schoolmaster shook his head, but his face was sullen.

"Then take your verses down, man," said the Parson. "And be careful in the future not to accuse anyone unless you are certain of guilt."

But Abigail was remembering the clatter on the floor when Mrs. Simpson had left her pew. Had the foot warmer been upset? Had some of the coals fallen out? Were the Simpsons to blame for the fire, after all?

It was the next morning, however, after her lessons, that Abigail spoke of this to her father. "But I am not sure that the noise I heard was the warmer being overturned," she said carefully.

"And neither am I sure," said Parson Smith, "so we'll say nothing more about it.

Henry Simpson is a good man. He would be grieved to think he had set fire to the meeting house."

The Parson puzzled a minute. "The coals could have smoldered and set the dry wood on fire. Simpson might not have noticed when he came back after the service. However, this is the way I shall write it down in my record."

He picked up his goose quill pen and wrote: "Weymouth Meeting House took fire on April 23, 1751. Burned to ground in 2 hours. 3bbls. of gunpowder, the town stock, blew up with great noise. Uncertain how it happened."

CHAPTER 3

Grandmother Quincy's House

When our guests arrive, Abigail," said Grandmother Quincy, "they will greet me first. Then I shall present them to you. Now that you are thirteen, you should meet young ladies and gentlemen."

Abigail listened seriously. She was visiting at Mount Wollaston, the Quincy's home in Braintree (see map, page 188). She loved visiting her mother's parents. The library was filled with books and newspapers. Besides, Grandmother Quincy had many servants, and so there was time to read and to visit.

"What shall I do when I am presented?" asked Abigail.

"Curtsey, as I have taught you, and offer the gentlemen your hand. And remember to speak softly and not be noisy."

Since she was a little girl, Abigail had been taught good manners by her grandmother. She had learned these same lessons from her mother. But the parsonage had only two servants. At home, Abigail helped with the spinning, weaving, soapmaking, and care of the dairy. She no longer had lessons with her father. But she had read most of the books in his study.

"Whom have you invited?" she asked.

Grandmother Quincy ticked off the guests on her fingers. "Our former neighbor John Hancock. Your cousin Dorothy Quincy. Joseph Warren. Oh, and John Adams. He was at Harvard with the other boys. He teaches at Worcester, but he's home now for the summer holidays."

Abigail looked relieved. There would be only one stranger. Dorothy was about her own age. The young men were older, but she had known them since she was a child.

"Doesn't John Adams live in Braintree?" she asked.

"Yes. About a mile from here. His father is only a small farmer, but he managed to send John to Harvard. He's the oldest son."

"I suppose his father expects him to be a minister," said Abigail. She knew that the oldest son in nearly every New England family studied for the ministry, if his family could afford to send him to college.

"John's studying law now," said Grandmother Quincy. She shook her head. "He'll not get very far that way. People in Massachusetts don't think much of lawyers."

"Why not?"

"They earn most of their fees by helping the dishonest."

"Sometimes people are accused falsely and need a lawyer," Abigail protested.

"Not often," answered her grandmother. "But we'll get the tea things ready now."

She arranged the silver tea service on the small table. "I'll pour the tea, and you can pass the plate of seed cakes," she instructed.

Abigail watched her grandmother measure the tea and put the copper kettle on the fire. The rich silk of her full-skirted gown gleamed through the delicate lace of her shawl. The cap to match rested lightly on her snow-white curls. Her small white hands moved gracefully among the tea things.

"How lovely she looks!" thought Abigail.

There was a sound of coach wheels outside and then the clopping of horses' hoofs. In a few minutes, Abigail was sedately curtseying and welcoming the visitors.

The tea and seed cakes were passed. Everyone clustered around the fireplace. Abigail sat in the farthest corner, for she was the youngest. Dorothy Quincy moved over toward the young men. She was only a little older than Abigail but much more grown-up in manner. She was small and lively, with dark hair and eyes, a pert nose, and a pointed chin. Already someone had asked her hand in marriage. Now she sat looking demurely at John Hancock.

Abigail studied the three male guests.

John Hancock was the son of Reverend Hancock, who had been the minister at Braintree until his death in 1744. When John was seven, he had been adopted by his Uncle Thomas, who was rich and childless. John lived most of the time now in Boston. He was thin and nervous and slightly stooped. As usual, he was dressed very richly, and today wore a red velvet coat with gold buttons and a fine wig tied with a big black bow.

Joseph Warren was the youngest of the three and was still attending Harvard. He planned to be an apprentice to Doctor Lloyd, so that he could study medicine.

Perhaps because he was a newcomer, Abigail was more interested in John Adams, who was the oldest of the three. He also had blue eyes and light-brown hair. But he was short and stocky, with a powerful neck and shoulders. He was the merriest and most talkative of the group. He had a rich, deep voice and a hearty laugh.

The entrance door slammed.

"That's my husband," said Grandmother Quincy. "He was in Boston today."

Colonel John Quincy strode into the room. He was tall and white-haired, but walked and talked with vigor. The young men rose respectfully, and the girls curt-seyed, for Colonel Quincy was one of the leading men in Massachusetts. He had been active in government and a colonel in the local militia.

"What news from Boston, sir?" asked John Hancock.

"Lord Jeffrey Amherst and his troops will land tomorrow," said the Colonel. "His ships are idling in the harbor now, so that Boston can give the men a proper welcome."

"We'll have victory soon, now that Wolfe and Amherst are in command," said John Adams.

"Our new prime minister, William Pitt, can be thanked for that," said the Colonel. "He is the one who has sent us young and able officers."

"And we Americans are willing to fight,

now that our officers get the same rank and pay as the British," said John. "I read in the *London Gazette* about the fight Pitt had in Parliament to get that measure passed."

The Colonel looked at John Adams with interest.

"Grandfather likes people who read," thought Abigail.

Abigail was listening carefully. The young men had forgotten the girls. Dorothy pouted a little and played with the folds of her red silk gown.

But Abigail had sat on the stool at her grandmother's feet and listened too often to the talk in this room not to understand what was being said. The English, she knew, wanted to move westward and get farm land on the other side of the mountains. But the French not only claimed Canada, but the Mississippi Valley as well. Because the English made farms out of the hunting ground of the Indians, the Indians were on the side of the French.

The wars between the French and the

English had gone on now for nearly fifty years. There had been King William's and Queen Anne's Wars, and now King George's War. The English had been losing at first. But since Pitt had become prime minister, things had changed.

"What are the plans?" Joseph Warren asked eagerly. "I hope the fighting won't be over before I finish at Harvard."

"You'll have time to fight," laughed the Colonel. "Wolfe is to move against Quebec, and Amherst is to go by way of Lake Champlain to Montreal, and then join Wolfe."

"We'll have all of Canada then," said John Hancock gleefully. "My Uncle Thomas will be glad of the trade in furs and dried fish."

"Once we're free of the French and Indians, we'll no longer need England to protect us," said John Adams thoughtfully.

Abigail looked at him in astonishment. How ungrateful! It was like a son planning to desert a mother who had cared for him all during his childhood.

"England will never let go of her colonies," said the Colonel. "We're her bread and butter. And why should we want to break away? We've prospered under her rule, and have the rights of English-born citizens."

"Her navigation laws stop our trade," said John Adams.

"Not too much," said John Hancock with a grin. "There's more smuggling going on now than the British even guess."

"He should know," thought Abigail. "His uncle owns the second largest wharf in Boston."

"If the population continues to grow in the colonies, all of Europe will not be able to hold us," John Adams continued.

"He is a very stubborn person," thought Abigail. "Or maybe he just insists that what he thinks is so."

She could see that her grandfather liked John Adams, even though they disagreed.

"You make us out too strong," said the Colonel, "even if I thought we wanted to be free from England."

"The only way we can be held down is for something to keep us from being united," said John Adams firmly. "But with thirteen governors and thirteen assemblies, I doubt if we'll ever work together against a common foe."

"You're right there. It's hard even to unite the people of New England," said Grandmother Quincy.

She had been listening to the discussion, nodding her head and saying a word now and then. Abigail hoped that she would someday be like her Grandmother Quincy. Grandmother was a gracious lady at all times, but full of gay chatter about the stories she read in the newspapers.

A servant came in and lit the candles. While the guests made ready to leave, the young men still busily talked to the Colonel. He walked with them to the entranceway.

"I'm afraid our young ladies were quite forgotten," the Colonel said after the guests had left. "Talk of wars and politics is not the way to get a husband."

"I doubt if any of those young men are thinking of marriage," said Grandmother Quincy.

"I talked to Adams a bit about his plans for the future," said the Colonel. "He expects to go to Boston soon to get his license to practice law. 'No girls, no guns, no cards,' he told me. He wants to give all his time to making good in his profession, and marriage would clip his wings. Anyway, he says he wants a thinking, reading woman."

Abigail smiled a little. John Adams must be the only one in Massachusetts who wanted a "thinking, reading woman." They were scarce enough. Most of the girls she knew had never gone beyond the Dame's School. It was not fashionable for a girl to be educated. Abigail's father and her Quincy grandparents were the only ones who did not frown when she buried her head in a book.

"I shall go to Boston tomorrow to see Amherst land," said the Colonel to his wife. "Would you like to go, my dear?"

"I have the grape jelly to prepare," she

44

said. "But why don't you take Abigail along?"

"Oh, Grandfather! Please do," begged Abigail.

"All right. You can visit your Smith relatives in Boston. But you'll have to be up at dawn."

CHAPTER 4

The Crooked Streets of Boston

The sun was well up the next day by the time Abigail and Colonel Quincy came to the gate of Boston. A few country people were still going through the arched entranceway with their wagons loaded with produce, although the market bell was sounding its last notes.

"Shall we be on time, Grandfather?" asked Abigail.

Colonel Quincy nodded. "Amherst will want his men to spruce up a bit. We'll be there to see them."

They drove briskly over the Neck, the narrow, mile-long mud flat that connected

47

the peninsula of Boston with the mainland (see map, page 186). Then they moved more slowly on the cobblestones of the narrow, crooked streets.

"We'll get off at the end of Long Wharf," Colonel Quincy instructed his servant Job. "You can wait at The Crown."

Holding Abigail tightly by the hand, the Colonel made his way. His very height and fine presence made even those who did not know him step aside.

Long Wharf stretched two thousand feet into the sea. It was the longest wharf in Boston. Its big ships could land there even at low tide. On its north side were warehouses, shops, and counting houses. Ships of every type lined the south side: whalers, merchant vessels, ferries, small fishing boats, and now the tall-masted ships of the King's Navy that had brought the British troops.

Abigail sniffed the air. It was exciting, though not nearly so pleasant as the good sea air at home. Here there was a smell of dried fish, leather, lumber, citrus fruits, and

salted meats. Strongest of all was the smell
of molasses. The merchant ships had
brought it from the West Indies. It would
be made into rum and exchanged for slaves
in Africa.

The wharf was crowded with people this
morning. There were merchants and ship
owners in fine coats, lace ruffles, and powdered wigs. Bustling about were apprentices in leather breeches. The breeches were
full enough to be turned around so that the
apprentices would not wear them out when
they were sitting. Shoppers, clerks with ledg-
ers, and townspeople had come to see the
troops land.

"I wish I were as tall as you, Grandfather," said Abigail. "I'll never be able to
see."

"I'll find a barrel for you to stand on,"
the Colonel promised.

But a merchant friend just then invited
them to view the troops from the second
story of his warehouse. The bells of the
meeting houses were sounding a joyous wel-

come now. Up the narrow stairs went the Colonel, two steps at a time, with Abigail running behind him. In a minute, she was leaning out the window, with the Colonel holding tight to her cloak. "Hold on to the window sill," he warned.

To Abigail's right was the crescent-shaped harbor of Boston, the jumbled roofs of its buildings crowding to the very edge of the water front. The bristling steeples of the meeting houses were thrust like swords into the bright blue of the sky. And like the giant backdrop of a stage were the three

tallest hills of Boston: Fort Hill on the
south, Beacon Hill in the center, and Copp's
Hill on the north. At the top of Beacon
Hill was the beacon, a tall pole topped by a tar
barrel filled with turpentine to light when
danger was near.

The clamor of the bells grew louder now.
Then came the roll of drums and the shrill
whistle of the fifes. "Here they come! Here
they come!" went the cry up and down the
wharf.

Line after line of marching men went by,
with their officers mounted on fine-groomed

steeds. The long-tailed red coats of the men with their spotless white crossed bands, waistcoats, and breeches were dazzling in the bright sunshine.

Finally, at the end, on a great bay horse, rode Lord Jeffrey Amherst, splendid in scarlet, white, and gold. He took off his plumed hat to the cheering crowd. A smile brightened his lean, hawk-nosed face.

"Hurrah! Hurrah!" shouted Abigail with the crowd. How proud she was to be English! How wonderful to have these gallant troops defend New England against the French and Indians.

"We'll find Job now and go to your Uncle Isaac Smith's house," said Colonel Quincy when the parade was over. "Since we're going to the North End, I'll stop at Paul Revere's shop. He's making a silver tray for your grandmother."

Through steep North End streets, narrow and crooked, Job drove the coach until he came to Paul Revere's silver smithy near the head of Clark's Wharf. The small-paned windows of the shop were filled with silver pieces glittering in the sun. There was a smell of charcoal from the furnace and the rat-tat-tat of a hammer as the Colonel opened the door.

Paul Revere looked up. "Good morning, Colonel Quincy," he called. "I wagered you'd be here to see Lord Amherst arrive. I'd like to have been there myself, but I had this teapot to finish for Mr. Hutchinson. He's giving a dinner for the officers."

" 'Tommy-Skin-and-Bones' will be bursting with pride at entertaining British noble-men," said Colonel Quincy.

Abigail knew that her grandfather did not think too highly of Thomas Hutchinson, the Lieutenant-Governor of Massachusetts. The Colonel presented her to Paul Revere. "She's a Quincy, all right," said the silversmith.

Abigail curtseyed to him. He was a fine-looking man, she noticed, sturdy in frame and of middle height. He had dark skin and eyes, strong features, and a wide mouth that showed good teeth when he laughed.

His full-sleeved linen shirt was open at the throat, and over it he wore a sleeveless woolen jacket. As he talked, he tapped lightly with his hammer on the teapot he was holding in his strong, delicately shaped hand.

"He must be French," thought Abigail. Nearly everyone in Massachusetts was of English descent and had fair skin and hair. But a few French Protestants, like Paul Revere, had ancestors who had come to America to escape religious persecution.

"Do you think Amherst and Wolfe will lick the French?" asked Paul Revere.

"They will, now that the New Englanders are willing to help them," answered the Colonel. "We were the ones who took Louisburg before, and by ourselves, if you remember."

"I fought at Crown Point in the last war," said Revere. "I'd like to go again, but I have a wife and child now, and the shop to take care of for my mother. But there's nothing like a fight to stir a man's blood."

"You've done your share of fighting," said the Colonel. "I'm glad you're here to be our silversmith."

"Well, there will be plenty of fighting before we take Quebec," said Revere.

"Do you have Mrs. Quincy's tray ready?" asked the Colonel.

"I've a bit more polishing to do. Can you wait?"

"I'll send my granddaughter to her Uncle Isaac's house," said the Colonel. "It's not far from here."

Abigail thanked the Colonel for bringing her to Boston. "It's wonderful to be English on a day like this," she said.

"I hope you will always have reason to say so, my dear," said the Colonel.

☆ ☆ ☆

"Boston is a lovely place to visit," said Abigail aloud as she opened the shutters of her bedroom in her Uncle Isaac's house the next morning. From the water front came the sound of hammers and saws and the smell of lumber, pitch, and paint. There were a dozen shipyards at the foot of Copp's Hill. Her uncle's house was on top of the hill.

Down on the street, criers were already calling their wares. "Fresh cod! Haddock! Mackerel!" called the fish peddler, blowing his tin horn in between his cries.

"Milk, oh! Milk below!" cried the milk-maid, shifting her wooden harness with its two copper jugs of milk.

"Sweep, o' sweep!" cried a small chimney

sweep, blackened with smoke, and bent with his burden of brooms and his torn blanket for the soot.

Everywhere was the sound of bells. Abigail heard them all day long. The market bells. The street peddlers. The shop bells. The town crier. School bells. Cow bells from the Common. The bells of the meeting houses calling to services, sounding alarms, ringing a welcome, tolling for the dead, or pealing out when there was joyous news.

"Boston is a town of bells," thought Abigail. This morning she loved their sounds and tidings.

There was a tap at the door, and the maid brought in a copper jug of hot water so that Abigail could wash.

"The mistress says you should hurry a bit," said the servant. "Mr. Smith wants to take you in his own boat to have a look at His Majesty's fleet."

"I'll hurry," said Abigail. What an exciting time she was going to have!

It was like this every day for the next two weeks. The Smiths loved to have Abigail come for a visit, and Uncle Isaac, who was a well-to-do merchant, had money and leisure to show her a good time.

Best of all, Abigail liked to go to her uncle's warehouse with her young cousins Isaac and Will. All kinds of spicy odors were in the air, and the floor was thick with the sawdust in which the fine porcelains from China and other countries had been packed. The workmen called the sawdust "bran," and things that were shipped this way were called "bran new."

"We'll go to the Common to see the soldiers before Lord Amherst leaves," suggested Uncle Isaac one day.

As they walked under the elms of the tree-shaded mall, Mr. Smith talked about the plans for winning the war. "Once Quebec falls, it will be over," he predicted. "Then with a few strokes of the pen in a treaty, all of Canada will come to England."

"Will New England get part of Canada?" asked Abigail.

"Of course. Colonial blood and money will be spent to win it. Canada belongs as much to America as it does to England."

That meant that New Englanders would start new colonies. Abigail remembered what John Adams had said. The population of America might be greater someday than that of England.

By the end of two weeks, Abigail began to tire of Boston. Her uncle's house was fine and large, but there were few books in his study. She began to feel crowded and pushed as she walked the streets. Some of the larger houses had gardens, but most of them were built close together. In the North End, especially, there were many houses that had overhanging second stories, and the narrow streets were dark and close.

The chill winds of October began to blow in from the ocean. Abigail thought of Weymouth and began to long for the open spaces and the glowing colors in the woods and fields. She wanted to watch the ocean with no other sound but its roaring waves and the shriek of swooping sea gulls, and no other smells but its salty tang.

"Boston is nice to visit, but I would rather be home," thought Abigail. She was happy when her father, perhaps sensing this and missing his favorite daughter, drove into Boston to bring her home.

CHAPTER 5

Courtship and Marriage

Abigail was in her father's study writing a letter to a friend, Mrs. Lincoln. It was early in October in 1761.

She wrote that there were not many gentlemen who called on her. "I believe you think they are as plenty as herrings," she wrote.

She smiled a little as she sprinkled sand over the page. "I'm seventeen. Old enough to be married," she was thinking.

She went on sleigh rides, picnics, country dances, and to singing school with the young people in Weymouth. She liked to have fun and took part in all the games. But few of the men called on her. Most of them, she knew, were afraid of a girl who was so much better educated than they were.

There was the sound of the knocker on the front door. Then Abigail heard familiar voices in the hall. Richard Cranch, who was courting Mary, was calling with his friend John Adams.

One evening while Richard had sat in the parlor with Mary, John had visited with her parents in the library. He had told them something about himself. He was past twenty-six now and had his license to practice law. His father had died and left him a house and farm.

Abigail had noticed her father give John a sharp look and her mother frown a little when he said this. After that, John had included Abigail in his conversation as she sat in a corner reading or playing backgammon with Betsey.

On his last visit, John had brought Abigail a gift of a book. "You are as shy as a deer," he had said when she had thanked him. "You hang your head like a bulrush."

But he had lingered to say this until Richard had called to him twice to come.

Remembering this as she heard John's voice now in the hall, Abigail flushed, and she quickly smoothed her hair. If only she could look into the small mirror in her bedroom upstairs. A minute later, her sister was in the study.

"John Adams has come with Richard to call on you," whispered Mary.

"But I'm wearing my old brown calico," said Abigail, using both hands now to smooth the wrinkles in her skirt.

"You always look lovely," said Mary.

Abigail did look lovely, even in the calico dress which she had made herself. The russet color of the dress warmed her dark eyes. Her brown hair was swept back like two wings on the sides of her face. She had a delicate nose and a soft, sweet mouth. Her small rounded chin was lifted and determined. She moved with grace and dignity, as her Grandmother Quincy had taught her when she was a little girl.

Reverend Smith and his wife were in the parlor when the girls came into the room. The Smiths had been happy when Richard had asked permission to court Mary, though she was a beautiful and popular girl. Richard had been born in England of a good family, and was now in a glass-making business in Braintree. Plans for the wedding already were being made.

Before the young men left that night, John Adams asked permission to speak to Reverend Smith alone. Abigail saw her mother's lips tighten. Richard and Mary exchanged smiling glances. But it was not until the next morning that Reverend Smith told about his interview with John. "He asked permission to marry Abigail," said the parson.

"He's only a lawyer," said Mrs. Smith sharply. "And his father was a small country farmer."

"But he is a brilliant young man. And I wouldn't be surprised if he does well with his future," answered her husband. He

66

turned to Abigail. "How do you feel about John, Abigail?"

"I like him very much," said Abigail shyly. She could feel the color warm in her face, but her heart was pounding happily. She knew that her father was on her side.

"Then I shall tell John he may continue to call on you," said Reverend Smith firmly.

"But there must be no talk of marriage for a long time," protested Mrs. Smith. "Abigail isn't strong enough. And Mary must be married first."

☆ ☆ ☆

It was almost three years before Mrs. Smith agreed to Abigail's wedding, which was on October 25, 1764. It was in the parlor of the parsonage, made gay with autumn fruits and foliage. Abigail wore a red and white sprigged woolen dress and a bright new cloak for going away. John was in dark-blue broadcloth and had on a white satin waistcoat embroidered by his mother in gold thread with sprays of wheat.

"I wish all my wheat were as free of rust
as this," John had said when his mother
had given him the gift. He was deeply grateful, but he found it hard, as always, to pay
compliments.

When the wedding feast was over, John
lifted Abigail up on his big brown horse, so
that she could ride behind him, like all
brides, to her new home. Judah, the Negro
servant Mrs. Smith had lent them, rode in a
cart with the chest of linen and woolen
things that Abigail had made while she had
waited for her wedding day.

"This is our home, dear wife," said John
when they came to his small house facing
the high road in Braintree. He pointed to
the green slope of Penn's Hill across the
road. "You can watch the sea from the top
of that hill," he said. "On clear days, you
can see as far as Boston."

North of John's house was the one in which
he had been born and where his mother and
younger brothers, Peter and Elihu, now
lived. The two houses were almost alike in

68

appearance and were quite old. They were
built of clapboards which had weathered to
a grayish-brown in color.*

* Both houses have been carefully preserved and furnished and are now open to the public. They are painted
a colonial red today.

John lifted the latch, and they were in the small entrance of his house. On the right was the parlor. On the left was John's study and office, for which there was an outside door. A narrow, crooked stairway led to the bedrooms on the second floor. The kitchen, in which they would also dine, was in a lean-to in the back. Above this was a bedroom for Judah, and storage space.

"I shall be happy here," said Abigail. Already, in her mind, she was placing some of her possessions in the rooms.

John loved to farm and did much of the work himself, though his law practice grew steadily. His mother and brothers liked Abigail, and there was much visiting back and forth. Mary and Richard Cranch lived nearby. Mount Wollaston, the Quincy home, was a pleasant walk from the Adams house in Braintree.

In July, 1765, the Adams's first child, a girl, was born. They called her Abigail, and then Abby.

One afternoon shortly after the birth of

Abby, John and Abigail Adams visited the Quincys. They talked about the Stamp Act which would go into effect on November 1, 1765. A stamp would have to be placed on all newspapers and legal documents. The money from the sale of the stamps would be used to pay for an army to defend the colonies.

"We've always been able to defend ourselves," said the Colonel angrily. "We don't need a British army, especially now that the French have been removed."

"The tax was passed without the consent of the colonies," added John. "We have no representatives in Parliament."

"But if our charters say we have the rights of Englishmen," asked Abigail, "why don't we have seats in Parliament?"

"Because the British insist that Parliament represents everybody in the British Empire," explained her husband.

John told about the anger of the people all over America and what they had done to resist the law. In Boston, men had hung a figure of the stamp collector from the tallest elm in the town. People then called it the Liberty Tree. At the end of August, a mob had broken into the home of Thomas Hutchinson, who was now Governor, and wrecked his furnishings. They had thrown the manuscript of his history of Massachusetts into the street.

"I don't like these deeds of violence," said Mrs. Quincy.

"But even though Tom Hutchinson was born in Boston, he has taken the side of the King and Parliament," protested the Colonel.

"There are better ways than violence," said John.

He told of the Stamp Act Congress which was meeting in New York. The delegates were discussing ways in which the colonies could work together to oppose the act. "That is the legal and orderly way," said John.

Abigail Adams was remembering how in this very room he had once said that England would not be able to hold her colonies if they would ever unite against her.

News of the Stamp Act Congress came to Boston. The members had resolved that there should be "no taxation without representation." They had agreed on a plan to boycott British goods and thus have the merchants of England force Parliament to do away with the act. Not a single stamp was sold in any colony. In May, 1766, news of the repeal of the Stamp Act came to America.

A little over a year later, Colonel Quincy died. It was the first loss of someone dear that Abigail Adams had known. But two days before the Colonel's death, on July 11, 1767, her first son was born. He was named John Quincy, in honor of his great-grandfather.

"Our son will grow up in a free country," said John Adams. "The British made a stupid blunder when they passed the Stamp Act. Now that they know the character of the Americans, they will not try that again."

CHAPTER 6

The Boston Massacre

I should like to move to Boston," said John one day when they had lived more than three years in Braintree. "Cousin Sam says my practice would increase. Would you agree, dear wife?"

Mrs. Adams was more than willing. Although she loved their little home in Braintree, she knew that the ten-mile ride to Boston was hard for her husband. Besides, she realized that he was becoming important in the political affairs of Massachusetts.

At the end of April, 1768, they moved into a house which Mr. Adams had rented in Brattle Square, in the heart of the city. His office was on the ground floor.

The friends who shared John Adams's political views came often to the house. His
cousin Sam Adams was the most frequent
visitor. Sam's father had been a prosperous
brewer, but his son's whole interest was in
politics. He had held only minor offices, but
he had a great deal of influence, especially
among the working people.

John Hancock was another good friend.
He lived now with his widowed Aunt Lydia
in a great stone mansion on Beacon Hill.
When his Aunt Lydia died, Hancock would
be the richest man in New England.

In January, 1768, Parliament had passed
the Townshend Acts, which put a tax on tea,
glass, lead, paper, and painter's colors. This
time, the British government was determined
to have the law obeyed. In September, 1768,
two regiments of British troops came to Boston to enforce the collection of the taxes.
The citizens refused to house the soldiers.
Most of them were camped on the Common,
which was only three blocks from Brattle
Square. The roll of drums, the shrill notes

of the fifes, the clump of heavy boots on the cobbles, and the sharp cries of command were heard from early dawn.

"We never have a moment's peace," Mrs. Adams told her husband. "I cannot bear the sound or the sight of the camp."

She remembered the day when she had seen Lord Jeffrey Amherst ride into Boston. How proud she had been to be English! How loyal to her King!

"I'm proud now of my English birth. But am I still loyal to my King?" she wondered. With the other people of Boston, she fiercely resented the new taxes. But hardest of all to bear was the presence of the soldiers.

One day, she watched a group of boys yelling at the red-coated soldiers as they marched stiffly back and forth.

"Lobster backs! Lobster backs! Bloody backs!" cried the boys. Some threw stones.

An officer on a big brown horse came clattering to the square. The boys fled through the alleys, but turned once more to jeer at the guards and then run again.

"Those boys will start trouble," thought Mrs. Adams. "I must keep John Quincy in our own small yard."

It was a year and a half before that trouble came. On March 5, 1770, Mrs. Adams watched the snow fall in thick white flakes. She felt tired and listless. Just a month before, Susannah, her third child, had died. She was buried now in Braintree. It was one more tie to the little farmhouse for Abigail Adams.

The sun came out by noon, and Mrs. Adams let Abby and John Quincy go out to play. She thought the snow drifts would keep the soldiers in their barracks and the rough boys off the streets.

The children were hungry and tired by sunset. "You'll sleep well tonight," said their mother, as she put them to bed after their supper. The house would be quiet. Mr. Adams was going to his political club in the South End of Boston. She would read in front of the fire in the parlor.

So absorbed was Mrs. Adams in her book,

that she heard only vaguely the cries of people and the sound of running feet. Then suddenly church bells began to ring from all directions.

"There must be a fire!" she cried. She ran to the window that looked over the street.

She leaned far out, but there was no glow in the sky. The street was filled now with men and women running toward King Street, on which the Town House faced. Some carried leather fire buckets. Others were armed with fire tongs, shovels, heavy sticks of wood, and even muskets.

"Town-born turn out! Town-born turn out!"

Shrilly, the cry went up and down the street.

Mrs. Adams's hand flew to her throat. It was the dreaded cry of the Sons of Liberty. She was afraid of the Sons of Liberty. They were a secret society whose members wore medals engraved with a picture of the Liberty Tree. Their purpose was to fight against the unfair laws of Britain. But many of the members were rough men who were only looking for an excuse to take the law into their own hands.

"What has happened?" Abigail Adams called to those going by.

But no one paid her any attention except one man who looked back and shouted something about "soldiers in King Street."

Abby and John Quincy, sleepy-eyed and frightened, came running down the stairs. Sukey, the maid, and Jonah, the house boy, hurried after them.

"What's up, Mistress?" cried Jonah. "What's up?"

Abigail stood motionless, for suddenly there was the crackling sound of gunfire. The few stragglers in Brattle Square stood

stock-still, then began running toward King Street.

Mrs. Adams pushed Jonah toward the door. "Go to the Town House! See what has happened! And look for your master!"

John! Where was he? Could he have gone to King Street and been caught in the mob? Had a bullet struck him down?

She tried to soothe the children and pulled

them close to her, for the cold air rushed through the open window.

Sukey fell to her knees. "Lord save us!" she prayed.

Before long Jonah rushed back. "The lobster backs fired on the crowd in King Street. There's been a bloody massacre!" he shouted. "There's blood all over the street."

"Did you see your master? Did you look for him?" cried Mrs. Adams, frantic with fear.

"I couldn't see anybody in the crowd. I'll go back, ma'am," answered Jonah, glad of an excuse to return.

Where was John? He would not stay indoors with all of Boston on the streets. A roll of drums had started. It was the signal for the soldiers to assemble. They were running now toward King Street, bayonets fixed, boots clattering, the rumble of the drums growing louder and louder.

"Papa! Papa! I want my papa," cried John Quincy.

Little Abby wailed loudly.

John! John! Where are you? Abigail bit her lips so as not to cry the words aloud as she drew the children close. Then she saw John running toward the house down the dark street. His cloak flew wide, and his little lantern was dark.

Mrs. Adams took the children by the hands and opened the door of the entrance hall. "Your papa is coming," she said.

In another minute, Abigail and the children were in John's arms.

"What happened?" begged Mrs. Adams, after Sukey had taken the children to bed. "Jonah said the soldiers fired on the crowd."

"That's right. Five men are dead or dying, and a dozen wounded."

"And where were you? Oh John, I was so frightened!"

"I was with the men in my club. We heard the bells and ran out with our fire buckets. I followed the crowd to King Street and heard the news. They were taking the bodies away, but the snow was still splashed with blood."

"How did it happen?" asked Mrs. Adams. Quickly her husband told what he had learned. Boys and men had been throwing snowballs and making fun of the one sentry in front of the Town House. The soldier had called for help, and Captain Preston, the British officer of the day, and seven of his men had come to the sentry's aid. No one knew who had given the order to fire. There had been one volley. The mob was hushed with horror by the time Mr. Adams had come. Then drums had begun to roll, and the troops had arrived.

"I rushed home then. I passed the soldiers without taking any more notice of them than if they were marble statues. I wanted only to know that you were safe."

There were voices in the street now, and the door slammed as Jonah rushed into the house. "Oh, Master! I'm glad to see you!" he cried.

"What's going on in King Street?" asked Mr. Adams.

"The people are going home. Governor

Hutchinson came to the square," said Jonah, still breathless from his run. "He asked the people to go home. He said Captain Preston and the soldiers would be put in jail and brought to trial at once. It was a bloody massacre, sir. They'll be hanged for this."

"What will happen now? What can come of this night but sorrow and more bloodshed?" asked Mrs. Adams.

But not even John could answer that.

He had more news, however, when he came home the next day. There had been sober men in the crowd in King Street who had tried to get the mob to break up, he said. But the leaders had jeered at the soldiers and dared them to shoot. It was still not known who had given the order to fire. Certainly, it had not been Captain Preston.

"There will be more rioting and bloodshed as long as the soldiers are here," said Mrs. Adams.

"They will be gone in a day or so," her husband told her.

Sam Adams and a group of citizens had

gone to Governor Hutchinson and demanded that the soldiers be removed from Boston. The Governor had at last agreed, and the troops were to be withdrawn to Castle William, a fort on an island in the harbor. Preston and the eight soldiers would remain in jail.

"Will they be tried soon?" asked Mrs. Adams.

John Adams nodded. "But I shall be in the thick of it," said he. His face was troubled as he looked at his wife.

"What do you mean?"

Adams told how a friend of Captain Preston's had come to him and begged him to defend the Captain and the other soldiers. All other Boston lawyers had refused to take their case, except Josiah Quincy, Abigail's young cousin. He had said that he would help if Adams would take the case.

Mrs. Adams's face grew a little pale. "Boston people will say you are a Tory," she said slowly.

"I may be called a Tory," said John

Adams, thrusting out his chin stubbornly. "But in a free country, a man accused of a crime is entitled to have a lawyer to defend him. I hope, dear wife, you agree with that."

"It is the only thing you could do," said Mrs. Adams. "We will show the world that we are a just and law-abiding people."

The citizens of Boston were in two political parties. Those who believed that the King had the right to rule called themselves Tories, like the King's party in England. Those who believed that Parliament should control and who also wanted representatives from American colonies to be in Parliament were called Whigs, as they were in England.

For months, John Adams and Josiah Quincy worked on almost nothing else but the case of the British soldiers. They questioned ninety-six witnesses, in the hope of getting someone without prejudice who would say that the soldiers had been forced to fire in order to defend themselves. It was August before the case was tried. Tempers had cooled by then. It was now agreed that

a mob and not the good citizens of Boston
had made the attack.

Abigail Adams sat in the audience while
the soldiers were being tried. The courtroom
was filled, for this was an important case.
The four judges wore their crimson robes

and full wigs. The red uniforms of the
accused soldiers, who were sitting pale and
quiet in their places, made a great blaze of
color.

Her heart filled with pride, Abigail heard
her husband prove that the soldiers were not

murderers but had fired in the performance of their duty. John was in his black robe and full white wig, so that one could not see that his brown hair was growing thin and that his forehead was bald. He was heavier now than when he and Abigail had been married. His color was high, and his blue eyes sparkled with feeling as he pleaded his case in court.

John's best defense was the testimony of Patrick Carr, an innocent bystander who had been mortally wounded. Patrick had lingered in great pain for ten days before his death. But he had given a statement to the doctor who had attended him.

"I bear no grudge," Patrick had said. "The soldiers only did their duty. They fired in self-defense."

The trial lasted for eleven days. The verdict was "not guilty as charged" for Captain Preston and six of the soldiers. The two who were proved to have fired were accused of manslaughter and branded on their hands for punishment.

After the verdict was given, the soldiers

crowded around John. "You are a brave and honest man," said one, speaking for all. "We owe our lives to you."

"The jury did exactly right," John said later to Abigail. "And come what may, this was the best action of my life."

CHAPTER 7

The Boston
Tea Party

In the last week of November, 1773, a ship, the *Dartmouth*, arrived in Boston with a cargo of tea from England. The Townshend Acts had been repealed, and taxes had been lifted from all imported goods except tea. The *Dartmouth* belonged to the British East India Company, which had almost no money. Parliament wanted to keep the company in business, so it passed a measure allowing the company to export tea without paying a heavy export tax. In this way, the company could sell its tea in America cheaply, even though the colonists would still have to pay a threepence-a-pound tax.

"The Americans will surely start drinking

tea now," the members of Parliament had said. "It will be cheaper than any they can smuggle on Dutch ships."

"We'll not drink a mouthful," said the colonists, at least those who were Whigs. "It's not the price of the tea to which we object, but being taxed without our consent."

The day after the *Dartmouth* pulled into the harbor, signs were posted on trees and walls.

"Friends! Brethren! Countrymen!" they read. "That worst of plagues, the detested tea, is arrived. Every friend to his country is now called upon to meet at Faneuil (*fan' l*) Hall at nine o'clock this day. The bells will give the signal."

The meeting was crowded. Plans to keep the tea from being landed were made. Samuel Adams and a group of citizens called upon Mr. Rotch, the owner of the *Dartmouth,* and insisted that the ship be tied up with its cargo unloaded at Griffin's Wharf.

"What will happen now?" Abigail Adams asked her husband.

"They will not land the tea," he said firmly. "There will be civil war if they do — or worse."

"What could be worse?"

"The loss of our freedom."

The Adamses had moved to a house which John had bought on Queen Street. There were now four children in the family.

Charles had been born in May, 1770, and Thomas in September, 1772. Abby and John Quincy were old enough for the Dame's School, but because of the troubled times, Abigail was teaching them at home.

Days went by. Governor Hutchinson had told Mr. Rotch that the *Dartmouth* could not leave the harbor unless it was unloaded. If this was not done in twenty days, said the Governor, its cargo would be seized by the customs officers. But an armed guard of citizens watched the *Dartmouth* day and night so that it could not be unloaded. Every other night, John Adams took his turn at guard. Now two other ships, also carrying tea, were tied up at Griffin's Wharf.

Then came Thursday, December 16, 1773.

"Tomorrow the twenty days will be up," said Mrs. Adams to her cousin Will Smith, who came to tell her the news. John was away on a business trip. "What is going to happen?"

"We're going to have salt-water tea tonight," said Smith with a grin. "I've come to borrow your old red blanket." Mrs. Adams looked startled, but she gave him the blanket.

"Don't be frightened, Cousin Abby," said Will. "Nothing will harm you. I'm off now to the Green Tavern."

All of Boston seemed to be on the street that day. Jonah ran back and forth to tell his mistress news of what he heard. Men and boys were collecting blankets and long feathers. Wives were scraping the soot from the fireplaces and lamps. As evening came, most of the men and boys were gathering in the Green Tavern or in the long room over Edes and Gill's printing shop, where the *Boston Gazette* was published.

"They're saying Boston harbor will be a big salt-water teapot tonight," said Jonah, his eyes popping with excitement. "There will be no curfew tonight, Mistress. If you let me go out, I can tell you what happens."

"I'll see. I'll see," Mrs. Adams promised.

At dusk, she stood wrapped in her cloak in the doorway of her house. Cousin Will Smith stopped by. There were smears of soot on his face, and he carried the Adams's red blanket.

"Sam Adams has called a meeting in the Old South Meeting House," said Will. "Everybody's waiting to hear from Mr. Rotch. He's gone once more to Governor Hutchinson to ask permission to have his ship leave the harbor with its cargo unloaded."

"And if the Governor refuses?" asked Mrs. Adams.

"Sam Adams will give the word," said Smith. "I'm off now."

In a little while, Jonah came running home. The Old South was jammed, he said, and there were thousands of people outside.

"But I've a good place in the belfry from which I can watch," said Jonah. "I'll come back to tell you, Mistress."

Then he was gone.

Queen Street, which had been almost empty for a time, was filling now with hurrying people.

"What is happening? Where are they going?" Mrs. Adams wondered.

Then she saw Jonah running toward their house.

"Everybody's going to Griffin's Wharf," he cried. "The Governor said No to Mr. Rotch. Sam Adams gave the word. 'This meeting can do nothing more to save the country,' he said. I heard him plain as day."

"What are they going to do?" asked Mrs. Adams.

"I don't know yet. But may I go? You promised me."

"I'll go with you. Run upstairs. Tell Sukey not to leave the children."

Through the crowded streets, Mrs. Adams and Jonah pushed their way. "Boston harbor is a teapot tonight! . . . Hurrah for Griffin's Wharf! . . . Salt-water tea! Let's have salt-water tea!" were the cries around them. People were laughing and excited.

At the wharf, Jonah found a cask on which his mistress could stand. Pine torches flared everywhere. The wharf was already jammed, but the crowd pushed together to make way for men and boys wrapped in blankets, their faces covered with soot. Gay feathers were in their hair, and axes swung on their shoulders. They were gathering in three groups near each of the ships.

There were faces under the soot that Mrs. Adams thought she recognized. That stocky figure with the dark hair showing between the feathers. Wasn't that Paul Revere? And the lace ruffles of a fine velvet coat on a slim-figured man? Surely they belonged to John Hancock. And wasn't that the shaking, palsied hand of Sam Adams swinging an axe to his shoulder?

But there was never a name called from the crowd.

101

"Me know you!" grunted each blanketed figure as he approached his group.

"Me know you!" came the answer.

"That must be the password," said Mrs. Adams to Jonah.

There was a full moon in a cloudless sky. The great black hulks of the ships and their rigging were clearly etched in the shining light. In orderly manner, the men went up the gangway of each ship. The crowd watched silently, with only a murmur now and then to call attention to some act.

"Heap big salt-water tea party tonight," someone called jokingly, but there was no answering laughter.

The crowd saw the captains come on the

decks and hand over their keys with no protest.
Cabin boys ran for lights. In a few minutes,
the boarders had disappeared into the holds.
Soon the great chests of tea were being hauled
to the decks. There were crashing sounds.

"They're opening the chests," went the
murmur along the wharf.

Splash!

"There goes the first one over the side."

Now bobbing chests were everywhere in

the water. The fragrance of tea filled the air. The crowd watched silently.

"The tea has not been landed," said Mrs. Adams in a low voice. John had said that meant civil war. Would it happen?

A thin line of rose and gold was in the eastern sky now. Men started coming up from the holds of the ships. The first man came down the gangplank. Then more and more came, until all were off the three ships.

A fife started to play. The roll of drums began. In lines of four, the men started to march to the Town House with their axes swinging from their shoulders.

A window flew up in the Coffin House Tavern. "You've had a fine evening for your Indian caper," someone called angrily. "But mind, you'll have to pay the fiddler."

Mrs. Adams recognized the voice. It was Admiral Montague, the commander of the British fleet.

But the men in the marching line only yelled at him. "Come on down, and we'll settle the score tonight," one called.

Down went the window with a loud bang.

John Adams returned from his business trip the next day. As soon as he had heard his wife's story of the "tea party," he sought out Sam Adams.

At dinner, John had news. The tide had been low, he said, and there was tea along the shore as far as Dorchester.

"Was much destroyed?" asked Abigail.

"Nothing but the tea. About three hundred chests. Probably about eighteen thousand pounds."

"And who will pay the cost?"

John looked grave. "Boston will pay in some way, I am sure." Then his face brightened. "But whatever the price, it was worth it."

"I thought I saw Paul Revere and John Hancock, and, I think, your cousin Sam," said Abigail. "Were they among the Indians?"

John smiled a little. "I would not let Sam tell me names. But you may be sure, my dear, they were no ordinary Indians."

Mrs. Adams questioned her husband no more.

Boston learned the "price" in May when General Gage returned from England. Hutchinson was to go to London, and Gage was to be in full command as Royal Governor.

In a few days, Gage announced the punishment for Boston. The port was to be completely closed until the price of the tea was paid. The assembly would meet in Salem, and there would be no town meetings in Boston. Officers who committed crimes would be sent to England for trial. A much larger army was on its way, and the citizens would be obliged to lodge the soldiers in their homes.

"These are intolerable orders," cried John Adams.

Soon everybody in Boston was calling the new laws the "Intolerable Acts." Perhaps there had been some right for Parliament to levy taxes, but these laws had been passed only to punish Boston.

After June 1, 1774, not a ship moved in the harbor, not even the ferry which went from Boston to Charlestown.

"What will happen to Boston without trade?" asked Abigail. "The whole life of the town depends on it."

John nodded. He knew this better than his wife. Merchants, ship owners, sailors, and craftsmen who built the ships now would be out of work. His own law practice, which depended on this trade, would suffer.

"We'll have to move back to Braintree. We can't afford to live here," he said. "I'll not make a shilling a week."

"Is Boston alone to suffer?" asked Abigail.

"Perhaps not," said John.

Already, great wagon loads of goods were coming into Boston from other settlements by way of the Neck, the only land approach. And Paul Revere, on a swift horse, was riding to New York and Philadelphia with a full account of what had happened.

What would the other colonies do?

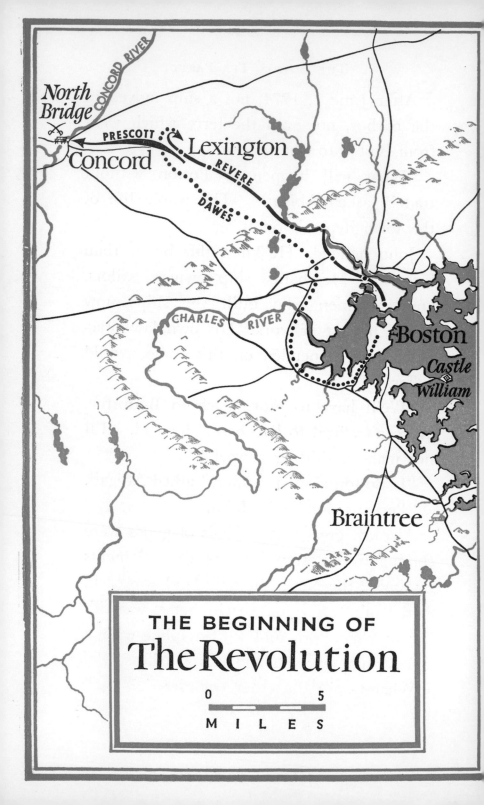

North
Bridge

CONCORD RIVER

PRESCOTT

Concord

Lexington

REVERE

DAWES

CHARLES   RIVER

Boston

Castle
William

Braintree

THE BEGINNING OF
The Revolution

0   5
MILES

CHAPTER 8

To Arms!

The rest of the colonies acted. "If it can happen in Boston, it can happen here," their leaders said.

A Continental Congress was called to meet in Philadelphia on September 1, 1774. John and Samuel Adams were two of the five delegates from Massachusetts.

In every New England town and village, men drilled on the green. They called themselves minutemen, for they were to act at a minute's notice. Bullets were cast in every kitchen. The gunpowder in the towns and villages was stored in secret places, for it might be seized from the steeples of the meeting houses.

"Courage we have in abundance, but powder — where shall we get a sufficient supply?" Abigail Adams wrote to her husband.

It was almost the middle of November before John came home from Philadelphia. Mrs. Adams had heard little news except that he was safe. Letters were difficult to send and cost a dollar by post.

Mr. Adams had gifts for all the children and a bright-blue silk cloak for Abigail.

"A dark color would have been more practical," she said, but her eyes were dancing.

"Slate-gray neither suits your face nor your spirit," said John, happy at her pleasure with the color.

John Adams was full of hope. Most of the delegates, he said, wanted to unite to resist the acts of Parliament.

"I am not a Virginian, but an American!" Patrick Henry had cried.

The Congress had a plan by which all merchants would be obliged not to buy or sell British goods. It had also sent petitions to the King and Parliament.

"We are sure that Parliament will repeal

the acts," said Adams, "now that the British know we are united." His chin grew firm. "If not, we will meet again next May."

☆　☆　☆

It was one o'clock in the morning on April 19, 1775.

A horseman pulled up in front of John Adams's house. Up flew the window. "What's going on?" cried Adams.

"The redcoats are marching to Lexington and Concord!" called the rider. In a moment, he was gone.

The bells in the steeple began to ring. Drums rolled. Lights shone in the windows of all the houses. In a half hour, there was the sound of clumping boots and of men's voices, as small groups of minutemen marched northward.

Mrs. Adams and Patty, her new and faithful maid, put on the big kettles and ladled out bowls of porridge and steaming mugs of coffee for the men who had come from a distance. The lantern hung high in the barn as John Quincy and his father fixed piles of hay on which weary soldiers could sleep for a few hours.

Bits of news were learned. General Gage had decided to send troops to Concord to seize the ammunition that was stored there. On the way, they would arrest John Hancock and Samuel Adams, who were in Lexington. The sexton of Christ Church in Boston* had hung two lanterns in the steeple to warn the people of Charlestown that the British were coming by water. Paul Revere had been rowed across the Charles River. He was to mount a swift horse and ride to Lexington. William Dawes, disguised as a farmer, had managed to get by the sentry at the Neck. The tolling of church bells had sent other riders along the coast.

As the day went on, fewer and fewer men went by. There was no more news, for no one came toward Braintree from Boston.

"What has happened?" A dozen times that day, John and Abigail Adams looked

* Christ Church is now referred to as Old North.

and asked that question. It was nearly midnight before straggling men returning from Lexington and Concord told fragments of what had occurred. No one knew the whole story.

"I'll ride as far as Concord and find out for myself," said John the next morning.

It was another day before he returned and told what had happened. Revere had reached Lexington and warned Sam Adams and John Hancock in time for them to escape. When the British had reached the town, a thin line of minutemen were waiting for them on the village green. No one knew who had given the order to fire. There was a flash of flame. In a minute, seven men lay dead, and ten were wounded. The rest broke ranks.

"It is the first time that British and American soldiers have fired on each other," said John slowly. "Now war has begun."

The British had moved on to Concord. Revere and Dawes had been captured by the British just outside Lexington, but Doctor Prescott, whom they had met, had managed

113

to escape the British and had carried the warning to Concord. The colonials there had held the North Bridge, and the British had not been able to advance farther. Later, Dawes also had escaped the British, and Revere had been set free.

A returning soldier told more news as he gulped hot soup in the Adams's kitchen. As the British had retreated toward Boston, hundreds of minutemen had lined the route and fired on them. At last, in panic, the British soldiers had broken their ranks and had run.

"They're shut up now in Boston, and our men are surrounding them," said the soldier. "I'll see my wife and children, and then I'm back to camp."

"And I have to leave for Philadelphia," said Adams. "Now there is no hope that King George will listen to our petitions."

Before he left this second time for Philadelphia, John held Abigail and the children close in his arms. "In case of real danger, fly to the woods with our children," he

114

urged his wife. "Do not let harm come to them."

☆ ☆ ☆

One Sunday morning late in May, the drums rolled, and the church bells rang a warning. Mrs. Adams ran to the window. Wagons were rattling southward along the high road, laden with people and goods. She called out to one driver, but she could not hear his answer.

In a little while, Peter Adams, John's brother, who was married now and living in his own home, was urging Abigail to leave with the children and come with him.

"Three British ships have landed near Weymouth," said Peter. "The troops may be here at any time."

Mrs. Adams's heart beat fast. *Fly to the woods with the children,* her husband had warned her. Then she heard men marching northward on the road. The minutemen were off to meet the foe.

"If the men can fight, we can stay," she told Peter. She called to Patty. "Bring water from the well. We'll make coffee and porridge."

Elihu, John's younger brother, and captain of the minutemen in Braintree, was home from camp. He helped Abigail serve food to the hungry men who were passing. She reached for her longest pewter spoon to stir the porridge.

"That's a fine thick spoon," said Elihu. "The men in my camp would give their ears for pewter like that. We haven't enough bullets at times to reload our guns."

Mrs. Adams stared for a minute. Then she rushed to the fireplace and began unhooking the long spoons and other utensils that hung there in a shining row. She pulled out the cupboard drawers and took out handfuls of tableware.

"Here. Take all my pewter," she cried. "We'll melt them now for bullets."

From the fireplace corner, Elihu took the big black iron soup kettle and put it on the logs. In a few minutes, the pewter spoons were thrust into the kettle, their long handles sticking out at a dozen different angles.

Little John Quincy came into the kitchen. He pointed, wide-eyed, at the kettle. "What funny soup!" he cried. "What are you doing, Uncle?"

"Making bullet soup," laughed Elihu.

"Bullet soup!" repeated John Quincy. Frightened tears were in his eyes. Then he looked at his mother. She was calmly pushing down the half-melted spoons to the bottom of the kettle.

She turned and smiled at John Quincy. "This is a great day for both of us, Son," she said. "We're helping to win the war."

Elihu was at the window. "Our men are back!" he cried.

"The British were gone when we got there," someone called from the road. "They came only to steal hay from the fields."

A glow was in Abigail Adams's face. She hadn't flown to the woods, and her children were safe.

The winter months went by. The few letters that came from Philadelphia were eagerly read. John Adams was impatient with Congress. Business was "as slow as snails," he wrote. He would like to see the colonies fight for independence. But most of the delegates still hoped to have the King and Parliament give them their rights. "I am shunned as if I were a leper when I mention independence," wrote Adams.

But Congress, though "slow as snails," took one good step. George Washington was made Commander-in-Chief of the Continental Army. His name had been proposed by John Adams.

"Now we are ready to fight," said Mrs. Adams when she heard the news.

CHAPTER 9

The Battle of Bunker Hill

The sun's up now over Penn's Hill, ma'am," said Patty.

All the children were huddled around the fireplace in the kitchen. A roaring sound rattled the window panes, and Patty's hand shook as she filled the kettle. Abby and John Quincy clung to their mother's skirt. Charles and Thomas began to cry a little.

"It's all right, children. Nothing will hurt us."

Mrs. Adams wished she could believe what she was saying. Since three o'clock in the morning, the house had shaken with the sound. At first, she had thought it was thunder. Then she knew. It was the roar of cannon.

"The war has begun!" she had cried, and jumped out of bed.

Now it was five o'clock on the morning of June 17, 1775.

"I'll go to the top of Penn's Hill and look toward Boston," she said, taking her husband's spyglass from above his desk.

"Let me go with you, Mamma," begged John Quincy.

Mrs. Adams smiled and took his hand. Up the steep hill they climbed. Beads of perspiration were on her forehead.

"It's going to be very hot," she said, moving toward a big flat rock under a shade tree.*

Even without the glass, Abigail could see smoke and fire coming from Charlestown, across the river from Boston.

---

* Today there is a stone on top of Penn's Hill marking the place where Abigail and John Quincy watched the Battle of Bunker Hill.

"Is this a battle, Mamma?" asked John Quincy.

"This is a battle, Son," answered Abigail gravely. "The day is come."

Where? Why? Who would win?

They went down the hill for breakfast.

"Is it dangerous, ma'am?" asked Patty as she put the porridge in the bowls.

Mrs. Adams nodded. "We'll eat our breakfast," she said, trying to be calm.

Later, Peter Adams came to the house to urge them to come to his farm. But Abigail said she would wait until the danger seemed nearer. Peter told what he had heard. The Americans had fortified Breed's Hill during the night because it overlooked Boston. They had planned to mount their guns on Bunker Hill but had missed it in the dark.

The hot day wore on. Somehow, at noon, the little family managed to eat dinner. "It's the warmest weather I have ever known," said Patty as she wiped her face with her big apron.

The firing grew heavier. Abigail could be

patient no longer. "If we go up the hill, we can see across the bay," she said, and took John Quincy by the hand.

The flat rock at the top of the hill was so hot by then that they could not sit down. They could see great clouds of smoke and long fingers of flame rising above Charlestown.

"They've set fire to Charlestown!" Mrs. Adams cried. She fell to her knees. "Almighty God!" she prayed. "Give strength and power to our people."

"Are the Americans winning?" asked John Quincy eagerly.

"As long as they can keep up this fire," said his mother. How long would that be? She knew the supply of powder was low.

A horseman galloped by their house. He paused, and Patty ran out with a water pail. Mrs. Adams and her son hurried down. There might be news of the battle.

Patty told them what she had heard. The British had crossed the Charles River about noon. General Howe was in command.

When his soldiers were safely across, the British had fired on Charlestown and set the town on fire.

All that night and much of Sunday, the sounds of the battle continued. In the afternoon, Peter came once more to beg them to leave with him. The Americans would have to give up, he said. Their ammunition was running low. If the British continued to hold Boston, they might move southward and reach Braintree. Again, Abigail Adams said she would wait.

At three o'clock, the gunfire ceased. But it was days before Mrs. Adams heard all the facts. The British still held Boston. They had made three attacks on Breed's Hill. With the third attack, the Americans were driven back because they had no more powder. The wind was blowing the heat and smoke from Charlestown into their faces, and they could not see to aim. But the British had lost eleven hundred men, one third of whom were officers.

"We'll be glad to sell them another hill at

the same price," said the hardy Americans. "We are dismayed, but not distressed," Mrs. Adams wrote to her husband.

At the end of June, General Washington came to take command of the troops around Boston. His headquarters were in Harvard Hall in the College. Mrs. Adams was invited to meet the General and his staff. He brought her a letter from John.

The winter passed. The British, Mrs. Adams learned, were hard-pressed for supplies. Washington's army closed them in by land, and the ships from England were captured or lost.

Early in March, 1776, Washington occupied Dorchester Heights, a peninsula south of Boston. Off and on for a week, the thunder of cannon rattled the windows of the Adams's house. On Saturday, Mrs. Adams and John Quincy climbed to the top of Penn's Hill.

"Look, John Quincy! Look!" cried his mother, handing him the spyglass.

Boston harbor was a forest of ship masts.

127

People were swarming on the decks. Supplies of all sorts were being loaded.

"Are the British leaving Boston?" asked John Quincy.

"They must be. But how could such a mighty army be conquered?" answered his mother.

Soon they learned the news. Washington's guns had kept the British fleet from aiding the army in Boston. On March 17, 1776, they sailed away, never to return.

Washington made a triumphant entry into Boston. Abigail wanted to see him, but there was smallpox in the town. Friends told her that their house on Queen Street was dirty but unharmed. But there was much destruction elsewhere. Even the Liberty Tree had been cut down for firewood by the British.

The move for independence grew stronger, John Adams wrote from Philadelphia. "People no longer treat me as if I were a leper." He sent Abigail a copy of a small book called "Common Sense," by Thomas Paine.

It gave in simple language the reasons why the colonists should seek complete independence from England.

News of the drafting of the Declaration of Independence came to Mrs. Adams in the *Boston Gazette* and in letters from her husband. He was on the committee of five men who drew up the written document, but he had insisted that Jefferson do the actual writing.

The written Declaration was adopted on July 4, 1776. From various people, Abigail learned how important John had been in the debates. A week later, she took the children to Boston to be vaccinated against smallpox. They were to stay in her Uncle Isaac Smith's house.

On July 18, Mrs. Adams went to church, then stood with the crowd in front of the State House.* She felt she had much to be grateful

---

* In 1776, the people of Boston began to call the Town House the State House, even though Massachusetts did not become a state until 1788.

for that day. The vaccinations had been successful, and today she was to hear the Declaration of Independence for the first time.

Her head was lifted proudly. She could hardly keep from telling those around her the important part her husband had played in having this document written. All eyes were on the little balcony off the council chamber from which the Declaration would be read.

Out came Colonel Crafts, who was in command in Boston. Other officials followed. The sheriff raised his hand. "A proclamation for independence of the United States!" he cried.

With a final clearing of his throat, Colonel Crafts began: "When in the course of human events . . ." and read on to the end: ". . . our lives, our fortunes, and our sacred honor."

"God save our American states!" shouted someone in the balcony.

"Hurrah! Hurrah!" roared the crowd, and a cloud of black, three-cornered hats flew in the air.

The bells rang. The soldiers fired their guns. Cannon boomed from the ships and forts. Bonfires flared high in the air. The King's arms were torn down from the State House. All other symbols of his reign were destroyed. On Sunday, the pastors read the Declaration from their pulpits.

Abigail wrote to John. "Thus ends royal authority in this State. And all the people shall say, Amen."

CHAPTER 10

The Adams Family in Europe

Each week John Quincy rode his father's big bay horse into Boston to bring the mail back to Braintree.

In November, 1777, he brought a heavily sealed letter to his father, who was then home on leave. It was signed by John Hancock, then the President of Congress. John Adams had been appointed to replace Silas Deane as a Commissioner in France along with Benjamin Franklin and Arthur Lee.

"I shall take John Quincy with me," said Mr. Adams, after the plans for his departure had been discussed.

"But he is only ten," said Abigail, her face a little pale.

"He is older than his years. And there are good schools he can attend in Europe." John put his arms around Abigail's shoulders. "I'll take good care of our son, dear wife."

Abigail smiled and held back her tears. "John Quincy needs a father's guidance," she said.

Three months later, from the top of Penn's Hill, Mrs. Adams watched her two men leave from the landing at Mount Wollaston. The next day, Abigail's uncle, Norton Quincy, who had inherited Mount Wollaston, brought her a letter which John had written just before he left for the ship. "The last thing John Quincy said was, 'Give my love to Mamma,'" Norton told Abigail.

She held the words close to her heart, trying not to weep for the husband and son who were gone from her.

Through the *Boston Gazette,* Mrs. Adams learned that the ship carrying her husband and son had landed safely in France. Six months passed before she received a letter

134

from John. He had written many, but they must have been lost at sea. The news he wrote was guarded. "There are many spies upon every word I utter, and every syllable I write," said he.

In August, 1779, John Adams and his son came home.

"My little boy has become a man," thought Abigail as she held John Quincy close. He was taller and even more serious than before.

"John Quincy learned to speak French like a native," said John. He shook his head. "I'll never be fluent in the tongue. Youth is the only time to learn a language."

Three months later, Congress gave John Adams a new appointment. He was to join Franklin in Europe to work on the peace treaty. This time, he took nine-year-old Charles with him as well as John Quincy.

"Charles also needs a father's guidance," said Abigail, but she held tight to Abby and Thomas.

In January, 1782, Charles came home with an officer of the United States Navy. Charles was too homesick and delicate to remain in Europe, John had written to his wife. John Quincy, however, had gone to Russia to be the secretary of Francis Dana, the first minister (official representative) to Russia from the United States.

Four years passed. In all that time, neither John Adams nor his son had leave to come home. Letters went back and forth, but they were still as scarce as ever. Much happened in the United States during that time. Cornwallis surrendered to Washington on October 19, 1781. In 1783, the peace treaty with England was signed, and independence was won. John Adams, Benjamin Franklin, and John Jay were the three men who made that treaty.

"If you had known that Mr. Adams would be away so long, would you have consented to let him go?" a woman friend asked Mrs. Adams.

"If I had known Mr. Adams would accomplish what he did I would have endured his absence for three more years," Abigail answered. She was sure that her two men would be able to come home, now that the peace treaty had been signed.

Then came a letter from John. He had been appointed to make commercial treaties with the countries of Europe. This time, however, he agreed to accept the appointment only if his wife and daughter would join him in Europe.

"If you and Abby were with me," he wrote to Abigail, "I could keep up my spirits. I am weary, worn, and disgusted to death. . . . I would rather chop wood, dig ditches, and make fences upon my poor little farm."

But Abigail was not sure that she should go.

She wrote to her husband that she didn't know the manners of court. "I was taught to say things I mean and to wear my heart on my face. I am sure I would make an awkward figure. I might disgrace you," she told him.

John brushed these arguments aside. He was the "happiest man on earth," he wrote.

He was making all arrangements for their journey.

With their two servants, John and Esther Briesler, Abigail and Abby sailed on the ship *Active* on June 20, 1784. The farm and house at Braintree had caretakers. Charles and Thomas had been sent to live with their Aunt Betsey, Abigail's younger sister.

The voyage from Boston to England took thirty days, and they were the most miserable Abigail Adams had ever known. The small boat rocked constantly, and the food was bad. At last, the passengers saw the white cliffs of Dover. Two days later, they were traveling by coach to London.

Mrs. Adams's cousin, Will Smith, was in London. When he learned that the *Active* had arrived, he ran all the way to the hotel where Mrs. Adams and Abby were staying.

"John Quincy waited as long as he could for you," said Smith. "Then he had to go to Holland to join Mr. Adams. But I've sent them word that you have arrived. In the meantime, I'll show you London."

Mrs. Adams was delighted with London. The buildings were impressive and the streets wide. The shops were filled with wonderful things. Every American in London came to call on them, and they had many invitations.

"This is a monstrous great city!" said Mrs. Adams. It was her first holiday since her marriage. She longed to see her husband and oldest son.

On July 30, when John Quincy was expected, Mrs. Adams and Abby stayed home all day. At tea time, their servant came pounding up the stairs. "Ma'am! Young Mr. Adams is come!" he cried.

A minute later, the door of the room was flung open. A slim, fine-looking young man wearing a freshly powdered wig and a well-cut broadcloth coat stood in the entrance.

Mrs. Adams stared. This couldn't be her little boy! But he was running toward her with both arms wide-spread. In another minute, they were all talking at once.

"We are to join Papa in Holland in ten

days," said John Quincy after a while. "You and Abby are to buy what clothes you need. Papa said that you are to spare no expense."

"Your father hasn't made a penny from his law practice since he came to Europe, and I know his expenses have been high," said his mother. She decided to be saving as always.

On the night before they were to leave for Holland, John Quincy took his sister to the theater. Mrs. Adams was in her room doing last-minute packing when she heard the door open. Her husband stood in the doorway. His wig was a little crooked. His clothes were dusty from travel, for he hadn't stopped to change.

For a moment, Mrs. Adams could not speak. She hadn't seen her husband in more than four years. She hadn't even heard from him in much of that time. Then he was holding her in his arms.

"I could not wait to see you," he cried. "I managed to get passage from Holland. We'll go to France from here."

How wonderful to hear John speak and be held in his arms! The years melted away. They were together again.

The Adamses reached Paris by the middle of August. Abby and her mother leaned out the windows of their coach as they clattered through the narrow, crowded streets of the city.

"I never saw so many people in one place, even on the Boston Common," said Abby, as they drove out of the city.

Mrs. Adams took her handkerchief from her nose. "Well, I may not have seen much of Paris," she said. "But I certainly have smelled it."

Her husband and son laughed. "Paris is a beautiful city, Mamma," said John Quincy. "Wait until you see the lovely gardens around the palaces that are open to the public. And we'll go to the theater, and the art galleries, and the ballet. You'll forget about the dirt and the crowds."

"I doubt it," said his mother.

Their new house, which Adams had rented

with furniture, was about four miles outside the city. It was a fine white stone mansion set in a large and beautiful garden.

"This must cost us a great deal," said Mrs. Adams, looking worried. She knew that her husband's salary had been cut and that Congress was allowing him very little for expenses.

"If we want our country to be respected, we must live with dignity," answered John.

As a thrifty New Englander, Mrs. Adams also objected to the eight servants on their staff besides the two who had come with her. She was annoyed, too, because the French servants insisted on doing only the work in their own special line. They listened politely to her requests, spoken in a mixture of French and English, then continued working in their own manner.

"I must make them understand me and do what I say, bad grammar or not," said Mrs. Adams with determination.

She wrote of her troubles to her sister Mary.

"There is one servant who does nothing but skate around the polished floors with waxed brushes on his shoes. The French never seem to think of using water. And over all the servants is one called a major domo. His chief concern seems to be that no one cheats but himself."

John laughed at Abigail's complaints.

"I think it wise to follow the customs of the country in which we are living," her husband told her.

However, there were pleasant experiences as well, for there were good friends living in Paris. Mr. Franklin lived only a mile away. Thomas Jefferson, who was also to work on the treaties, had just come to Paris with his daughter Patsy. She was attending an aristocratic convent school, but she spent every week end with her father.

The Americans also became close friends with the family of the Marquis de Lafayette. Although Madame de Lafayette belonged to the wealthiest family in France, she dressed simply and was charming in her manners.

She spoke English, and her children were
being educated to speak English. She and
Mrs. Adams were soon devoted to each other.

As John Quincy had promised, Mrs.
Adams and Abby went to the theater and
galleries, or strolled in the lovely public

gardens. Mrs. Adams disapproved, however, of the way the French people poured into the parks and countryside on Sundays. "Pleasure seems to be the chief business of life in France," she said, and kept her family at home on Sundays.

She and Abby soon learned that even the clothes they had bought in London were out of fashion. However, Mrs. Adams discovered a little dressmaker who had been an apprentice to Mademoiselle Bertin, the Queen's dressmaker. It was not long before Mrs. Adams and her daughter had new silk dresses that were just as fashionable and far less expensive than those worn by the ladies at court.

But Mrs. Adams did make one extravagant purchase when she ordered some new furniture for the big reception room of their home in France. The chairs were beautifully carved and covered with crimson damask. "There is nothing so fine as these chairs in Boston," she said. "And we can take them home with us."

146

She wondered, nevertheless, how the chairs would look either in the house on Queen Street in Boston or in the farmhouse in Braintree. Even Grandmother Quincy in her house in Mount Wollaston did not have anything so fine.

CHAPTER 11

First Minister to England

Early in 1785, Mr. Franklin resigned and went home to the United States. On May 4, letters came from Congress to Thomas Jefferson and John Adams. Mr. Jefferson was to succeed Mr. Franklin as minister to France. Mr. Adams was appointed as the first minister from the United States to England.

"I will have a difficult post," Adams said to his wife. "I don't know how the English will regard a minister from the nation which has just finished a war to win its independence from their country."

"There is no one better able to fill that post," said Abigail confidently.

She was not going to let her husband know how frightened she was at the thought of going to London as the wife of the new minister from the United States.

By this time, John Quincy also had made a decision. He planned to return to the United States to study law at Harvard.

The new appointment also meant a parting, at least for a time, from Thomas Jefferson. "He is one of the choice ones of the earth," Abigail said to her husband on the last day they saw Jefferson.

But their sorrow at parting from their son and good friends was forgotten in part when they thought of their own forthcoming problems. How would George the Third receive his new minister? Would the English people be unfriendly? Would Adams be able to start a good relationship between the two countries? Could he keep the dignity of his new and untried country?

"I know so little of court manners," worried Abigail Adams secretly, remembering the letter she had written to John before coming to Europe. "Who will tell me what to do? Am I going to disgrace my husband?"

But she hid her fears even from John.

"It will be a relief to speak the language of the country without twisting and twirling my tongue and pronouncing the words badly at the end," she said to her family, as she gave directions to her staff of servants to pack the crimson covered chairs for shipment to London.

Two weeks later they were in London and living in a house which John had rented on Grosvenor (*grohv' ner*) Square.

"How did the King receive you, John?" asked Abigail when her husband returned from his first audience with George the Third.

"He was very courteous, but I think he was moved by the meeting," said John, carefully taking off his freshly powdered wig and new black velvet coat.

"What did you say to the King?" begged Abby.

"Let your papa tell us in his own way," said her mother, though she was just as eager to hear the details.

John smiled at them. "I said I thought myself fortunate to have the honor to be the first American to be a minister to his court. I hoped I could restore the old good relations between two people who had the same language and blood."

"That was very diplomatic," said Abigail. She was proud of the way her husband had handled this very difficult first meeting.

"And what did the King say?" asked Abby.

"He said he was glad that I had been chosen to be the first minister, and that although he had been the last to agree to the separation of the two countries, he would be the first to accept the friendship of the United States."

A week later, Mrs. Adams and Abby were invited to meet Queen Charlotte. But their reception was not so cordial as the one given to Mr. Adams. The two American women stood nearly two hours before they were pre-

sented to the Queen, and the Queen did little to hide her dislike of them.

"I'll never again set my foot in the Queen's drawing room unless I have to," said Abigail to John, rubbing her tired feet when she was at home. "The King is a gentleman, but the Queen is certainly no lady."

The Adamses lived nearly three years in London. Their position was difficult, because of the unfriendly feeling of many of the English people. But John managed to build a good relationship between his country and England, and Abigail, in spite of her fears, made a charming and gracious hostess. However, she never again had a personal meeting with the Queen.

In the meantime, William Smith, John's young American secretary, courted Abby. He was well-educated and from a good family, and had been an aide to Washington during the Revolution. Both Mr. and Mrs. Adams were pleased with the match. The two young people were married in June, 1786.

In December, 1787, John Adams was given permission to resign his post and return to the United States. It was the following April, however, before he and Abigail were ready to leave England. By this time, the new Constitution of the United States was completed and was being approved by the states.

"It is only because of grinding need of each other that the states are agreeing to act together," said John. "I must do what I can to help that union."

He and Abigail were happy to be going home, for Abby and her husband also were to return to the United States. By this time, their first child had been born.

"I have seen high life," said Mrs. Adams. "But I feel I can return to my little farm and be happy."

However, the Adamses did not return to their "little farm" in Braintree. Before leaving London, Mr. Adams, through an agent, purchased Vassall House, a fine mansion in North Braintree. It had been built by Major Leonard Vassall, a wealthy West Indian sugar planter who had come to Massachusetts to live. The two-story house had a lovely garden, good stables, and separate quarters for servants.

Mrs. Adams, who knew the house, happily planned her furnishings. She would have the dark mahogany walls of the drawing room painted light gray and use the crimson covered chairs she had bought in Paris. The bedroom above would have green and white furniture with wallpaper to match.*

Everything worked out as planned. The Adamses landed in Boston, where John Quincy was waiting to greet them. He had finished his studies at Harvard, and was now an apprentice to a lawyer in Newburyport.

---

* The Vassall House is now called the Adams Mansion and is open to the public. It was the home of four generations of the family and was where both John, John Quincy, and Charles Francis Adams celebrated their golden weddings. Brooks Adams, who died in 1926, was the last of the family to occupy the house. It was made a national shrine in 1946 and is furnished today with the belongings of the families who lived in the house. The house was enlarged by John Adams.

The furniture arrived safely at Norton Quincy's wharf at Mount Wollaston, and John Quincy and his two younger brothers stayed five weeks to help get the family settled.

"Here I am at five o'clock in the morning, working on my diary," wrote Abigail Adams to her sister Mary. "How could I be happier?"

The New York Capitol Building

CHAPTER 12

The Second
First Lady

George Washington was the only man considered for the Presidency in the first United States election, in 1789. Each elector voted for two persons. All cast their first vote for Washington. Of the men who were a second choice, John Adams had the highest number of votes and so became Vice-President.

The first capital was New York City. Mr. Adams went there early in April, but Mrs. Adams remained in Braintree. She felt there were too many things at home that needed her attention.

"Leave the farm to the birds and beasts and come to New York," John wrote to her.

So, in June, Mrs. Adams hurried to answer in person her husband's impatient letter.

Their new home was a pleasant house on Richmond Hill overlooking the Hudson River. "I know I shall be happy here," said Mrs. Adams. "For once, I shall have nearly all my children near me."

Abby and her family also lived in New York. Charles and Tom would be with their parents. John Quincy was in Boston practicing law, but at least he was in the same country as his parents.

"My first duty is to call on Mrs. Washington," said Mrs. Adams, the day after her arrival. She ordered her carriage and drove to the large house where the Washingtons lived.

"I think I am going to like her," thought Mrs. Adams when they were introduced.

The President's wife, who was about ten years older than Mrs. Adams, was short and plump. She was simply dressed and wore a cap on her lovely white hair.

It was plain that Mrs. Washington also

liked her guest. "You know so much and you have seen so much," she said to Mrs. Adams. "You must tell me what to do. I am so afraid of making a mistake."

Abigail knew that although Martha Washington was a wealthy woman, she had traveled very little and had lived a simple life. "I hope you will stand next to me at all receptions," continued Mrs. Washington, "and go with me whenever you can spare the time."

"I am the simple wife of a lawyer," said Mrs. Adams. "I have not mingled much in high society except when we were in Europe, but I will tell you all I know."

In 1792, Washington and John Adams were re-elected. By this time, the capital had been moved to Philadelphia.

"I shall never be as happy here as in New York," said Mrs. Adams, although Philadelphia was the gayest city in the country.

Not only did she find the climate unhealthy, but she was now farther away from her children. Charles, who had married Sally

Smith, the sister of Abby's husband, lived in New York. President Washington had appointed John Quincy minister to Holland, and he had taken his brother Tom with him to be his secretary.

In John's second term as Vice-President, Mrs. Adams spent much of her time in Braintree. The section in which they lived was now called Quincy in honor of Mrs. Adams's grandfather.

By this time, Mr. Adams was becoming unhappy over politics, and so was President Washington. In their first term, the important men in politics had belonged to the Federalist party. Gradually, the views of some of the members changed. Under the leadership of Thomas Jefferson, they started a new party called the Democratic-Republicans. However, in spite of their political differences, John Adams and Thomas Jefferson continued to be good friends.

In 1796, Washington refused to run for a third term. He wanted to retire to his home in Mount Vernon, and he was unhappy about the way he was being abused in the newspapers. The race, therefore, was between the other great leaders. Again, each elector voted for two persons.

All of the Federalists did not vote for both their candidates. As a result, John Adams, the Federalist candidate, had 81 votes. Thomas Jefferson, the Democratic-Republican candidate, had 78 votes. For the first and only time in United States history, there was a President from one party and a Vice-President from another. After that, by an unwritten law, the electors chose men of the same party for President and Vice-President.

On February 8, 1797, the day on which John Adams, as Vice-President, announced the results of the election to Congress, Mrs. Adams wrote to her husband. Mr. Adams had gone to Philadelphia alone. His mother was very ill, and Abigail felt she should remain in Braintree, though this was the great climax of her husband's career. But how she wished she could be with him! She would try to tell him how she felt on this great day.

She hoped God would give her husband "an understanding heart" and that "the things which make for peace" would not be "hidden from" his eyes. Her feelings were not of pride upon this occasion, she told him. Her wish was that he would discharge his duties "with honor and justice to the country." This would be her "daily prayer."

Mrs. Adams left for Philadelphia in April. Congress had purchased a three-story house for the President on High Street, although no money was provided for its upkeep. Mr. Adams was so glad to see his wife that when the carriage drove up to the house, he ran down the flight of marble steps to greet her.

"I could have whipped up the horses myself, so anxious was I when I was on my way," his wife told him.

The next four years were difficult ones for John Adams. He was not as popular as Washington and could not afford to entertain on the same lavish scale. His salary was only $14,000 a year, and he had no allowance for expenses. But Mrs. Adams made a gra-

cious and charming First Lady. It was she whose cordial welcome put everyone at ease at the public receptions and made the people of Philadelphia feel more kindly toward President Adams.

Besides the widening differences between the two political parties, Adams had trouble with France during his term, because the French seized many American ships that were trading with England. However, the President managed to avoid war with France and made a satisfactory settlement of the dispute.

"If there is one statement I would like on my tombstone," said Adams, "it would be 'He made peace with France.'"

Thomas Jefferson and Aaron Burr were elected in February of 1801. The capital had been moved to the new city of Washington. Jefferson would not be inaugurated until March 4, 1801. In the few months that remained of the term of John Adams, he and Congress would meet in the new capital.

Mrs. Adams left Quincy for Washington

in October. President Adams was already on his way. However, she stopped in New York, for her son Charles was gravely ill. The day she left New York, she knew she would never see Charles again. Her one comfort was that Abby had taken him into her house and would give him every care.

On November 21, 1800, Mrs. Adams was seated in the smallest room of the new President's House in Washington. The biggest fire the servants had been able to build was burning feebly in the fireplace near her chair. She planned to write a letter to her sister Mary.

She shivered a little and drew her shawl close. "These plastered walls will never dry in this weather," she said half-aloud as she sharpened her quill pen.

The logs spluttered angrily in the fireplace, and the flames began to die. She reached for a bell rope to call a servant. Then she smiled. There was not a single bell rope hung as yet in the house. She opened the door and called to a man servant just coming into the hall with an armload of logs.

"Bring some dry wood, Sam, if you please."

"It's all wet and green, ma'am," said the servant.

"We're surrounded by forests. We should be able to get enough wood," said his mistress.

"We can't get anyone to cut and cart it, ma'am. There's no help here, except what folks have brought with them."

Mrs. Adams walked to the window while the man built up the fire. The house had a beautiful setting, she was thinking. It was three stories high and on a small hill overlooking the Potomac. One side faced a sloping meadow reaching to the main highway — Pennsylvania Avenue, it would be called. Mrs. Adams smiled. The "avenue" was full of mud holes now. In the rear of the house were small buildings as on most plantation homes, but as yet neither stables nor a coach house.

The servant came in again with more firewood. "Would you like to see the rooms that are ready, ma'am?" he asked.

Mrs. Adams went with him to tour the house. Only six of the rooms were finished, and even the main staircase was only half-built. One room, however, was lovely. It was oval in shape and on the second floor.

"I'll put my crimson furniture in here," said Mrs. Adams. "I'll use this room for our New Year's reception."

But the rest of the rooms either were bare or had wet plastered walls. Would they ever dry?

"We'll have to build more fires, Sam," she said when they returned.

"We have thirteen going now, ma'am," he said.

There was a knock at the door. A maid entered. "We have no place to hang the laundry, ma'am," she said. "There's no fenced yard."

"We'll find a place," said Mrs. Adams, putting down her pen.

With the maid, she peered into several half-finished rooms and finally opened the door of an immense room on the east side of the building. When finished, it would be the audience chamber. The East Room, it was to be called.

171

"We can hang the laundry here," she said. "The room is as big as a meeting house. But at least our laundry will be out of the weather."

There were no more interruptions as she

wrote to her sister Mary about her trip to Washington and the tour she had made of the house. Was there anything more to add? Yes, Mary would want to know about her health.

She was well, wrote Mrs. Adams, and so was her husband, "though the newspapers very kindly gave the President the fever. I am glad, however, that it was only in the paper that he had it."

"I must tell Mary to keep this letter in confidence," she thought, "or otherwise John's opponents will think I am finding fault with this house and Washington only because his term is nearly over."

She thought a minute before finishing her letter. Then she wrote. "Keep all this to yourself, and when asked how I like it, say that I wrote you the situation is beautiful, which is true."

There was another knock at the door as Mrs. Adams sprinkled the letter with sand. Sam came in with a message from Mrs. Washington. She had sent some venison and an invitation to visit at Mount Vernon.

The sun came out. The day grew cheerful. "Friendship can warm any place," thought Mrs. Adams, "even the President's House in Washington."

174

In February, Abigail Adams left for Quincy. Her husband sat up until midnight on the eve of Jefferson's inauguration on March 4, signing papers and making appointments. At sunrise, the out-going President ordered his coach and drove from the city. The bitterness of his defeat in the campaign of 1800 was too recent for him to wish Thomas Jefferson well on this, his first day in office. It would be many years before their old warm friendship would be renewed.

Peacefield

CHAPTER 13

Last Days

I shall never leave Quincy again," said Abigail Adams happily as she settled into the routine of living at home.

Her day began early. She rose at six and had breakfast at eight. Mr. Adams was off then to the farm, but she lingered until the servant brought the mail. "Perhaps there will be a letter from John Quincy," she would say.

At the urging of Washington, John Adams had made his son minister to Prussia. But with the election of Jefferson, John Adams recalled his son. In the fall John Quincy came home, bringing his mother a quantity of blue and white tiles from Prussia for a gift.

"I'll have them put around the fireplace in the west bedroom," she planned.

While he was in Europe, John Quincy had married Louisa Johnson, the daughter of Joshua Johnson, the American consul in London.

In time, John added a wing to Vassall House, which he now called Peacefield. He built another entry and a "long room" for receptions in which Mrs. Adams placed her crimson furniture. Above this was Mr. Adams's study. Here the walls were lined with book shelves. In one corner was the big desk he had used at Braintree. By the window was his favorite high-backed chair, gay with its covering of flowered chintz.*

There were always visitors in the house. Abby and her children came for long visits from New York. Tom was married now and living in his father's home in Braintree. Abi-

---

* This is the way the main house looks and is furnished today. The blue and white tiles are still in the west bedroom around the fireplace.

gail's nieces and nephews and cousins and their children lived in the neighborhood, and were always welcome.

On Sundays, there was usually a family gathering for noon-time dinner. In the morning, on good days, they all walked to church. In the winter or severe weather, they drove in the Adams's fine carriage. The townspeople greeted them with respect and affection. John Adams was still "the President" and his home "the President's house" to the people of Quincy.

There was leisure now for both Abigail and John Adams to write long letters. In time, many of these letters were written to Thomas Jefferson. Mrs. Adams began that correspondence. In 1804, Jefferson's daughter Polly died. Tears came to Abigail Adams's eyes when she heard the news. On the way to join her father in Paris, Polly had stayed with the Adamses in London. Mrs. Adams had loved her dearly and had never forgotten the golden-haired little girl.

"I'll write to Mr. Jefferson and tell him

179

that I share his loss," Abigail Adams decided.

A quick reply came to her letter, and soon Mrs. Adams answered. There were seven letters written, all filled with the give-and-take of politics. Then Abigail showed her letters to John.

"I think you should answer Mr. Jefferson's arguments," said she, "and show him that he is not nearly so democratic as he thinks."

Long, long letters were written by the two men to each other after that. They soon realized that their political differences were a matter of history. Each was more interested in what the other was doing — what people he met — how his family grew — what his opinion was of the issues and happenings of the day.

John Adams boasted of his family. He had thirteen grandchildren and four great-grandchildren. "These pretty little things disarrange my writing table," he wrote, "but give me much enjoyment."

The years went by. With pride, Abigail and John Adams watched the political career of John Quincy. He was elected senator from Massachusetts, and then made minister to Russia. He was head of the commission that made the treaty of peace ending the War of 1812. Finally, he was appointed Secretary of State by President Monroe.

"John Quincy is a chip off the old block," said the people of Quincy.

Mrs. Adams studied her face in the mirror. There were many fine lines, and the curls at her forehead were gray.

"You are as beautiful as ever," said her husband.

But Mrs. Adams only smiled. "If our glass flatters us in youth, it tells us the truth in age," she said.

"We must have your portrait painted," said Mr. Adams fondly. "Just as you are today."

The portrait was painted, and Mrs. Adams was pleased with the likeness. The delicate lace of her cap and shawl falling on the

181

The Abigail Adams Portrait

shoulders of her rich silk gown made her think of her Grandmother Quincy.

As she grew older, Abigail Adams spent much of her time in her west bedroom. It was sunny and warm and overlooked her garden. In summertime, the scent of the roses she had planted filled the room. Mr. Adams spent many hours with her in an armchair near the window.

Mrs. Adams's own chair was near the fireplace with its lovely blue and white tiles that John Quincy had brought her from Prussia. Near her was a table with her books and sewing. Her little dog Satan was on her lap or dozing at her feet. She still talked in a lively manner to the visitors who sat on the long sofa near her chair or the children who sat at her feet in front of the fireplace. But though she was always up and richly dressed, she rarely left the room.

In October, 1818, Abigail Adams became seriously ill with typhoid fever. John kept watch at the big four-poster bed. He knew there was no hope for his wife's recovery.

He wrote of his grief to Thomas Jefferson. "The dear partner of my life for fifty-four years now lies near the end, forbidden to speak or be spoken to."

About noon, on October 28, 1818, John was alone with Abigail, holding her hand. For a long time, she was silent, until he bent over and kissed her.

She opened her eyes and smiled. "Do not grieve, my dearest friend," she whispered. "I am ready to go. It will not be long." She did not speak again.

John Quincy Adams was not at home when his mother died. He was in Washington serving as Secretary of State. It was November 2, 1818, before he received a letter telling the news.

"Last Wednesday, the twenty-eighth of October, my mother, beloved and lamented more than language can express, yielded up her pure and gentle spirit to its Creator," John Quincy that evening wrote in his diary.

Her life was "filled with goodness and love," he continued. For fifty-four years she had been his father's "delight and comfort." He wrote then of the last time he had seen his father, and how John had said that he could not have lived through these years without the affection and cheerful encouragement of his wife.

"May I die the death of the righteous, and may my last end be like hers." Sorrowfully John Quincy Adams, who was to become the sixth President of the United States, closed the entry in his diary.

Old Boston

0 —————— ¼

MILES

Beacon Hill

Boston
Common

Liberty Tree

South End

The Neck

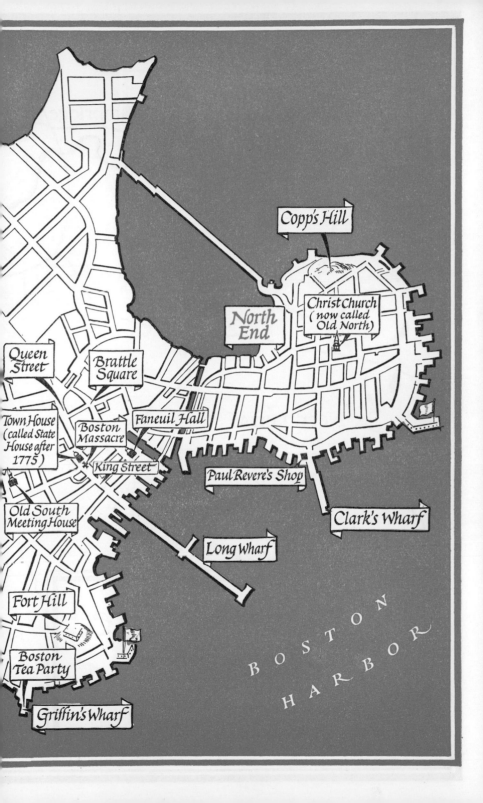

Copp's Hill

Christ Church
(now called
Old North)

North
End

Queen
Street

Brattle
Square

Faneuil Hall

Town House
(called State
House after
1775)

Boston
Massacre

King Street

Paul Revere's Shop

Clark's Wharf

Old South
Meeting House

Long Wharf

Fort Hill

B O S T O N

Boston
Tea Party

H A R B O R

Griffin's Wharf

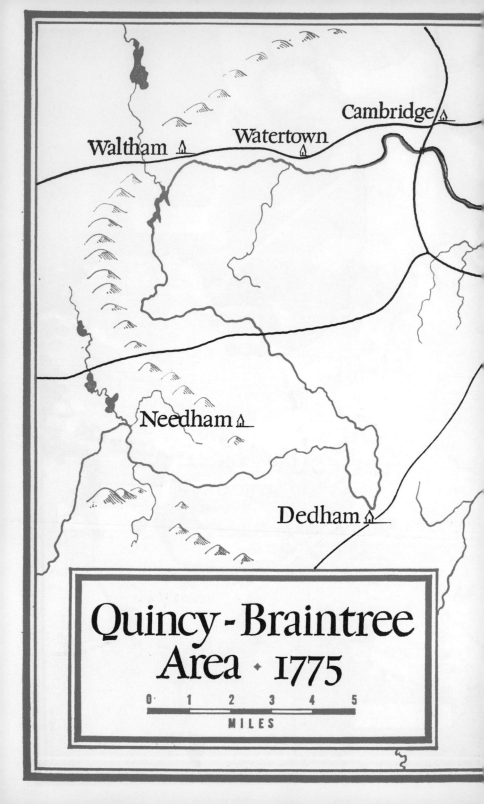

Waltham ⛪

Watertown ⛪

Cambridge ⛪

Needham ⛪

Dedham ⛪

Quincy - Braintree
Area · 1775

0   1   2   3   4   5
MILES

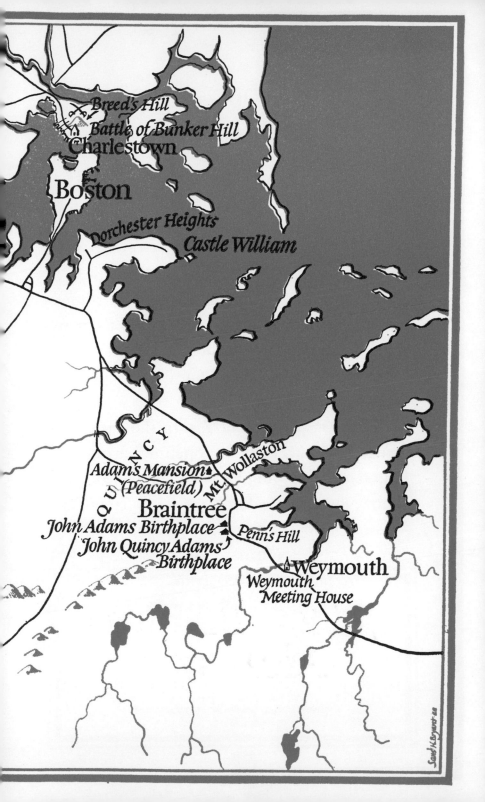

Author's Note

All of the events in this biography of Abigail Adams are true. The conversations in the book actually occurred or could have taken place, for they are based on things that were said either in letters or other written papers. Abigail Adams wrote many long letters to her friends and family, and everyone in the Adams family, except Abigail, kept full diaries.

The story of how the fire in the parsonage started as related in the opening chapters is based on what might have happened. We know there was a fire. The only record we have of it, however, is the entry made in Reverend Smith's journal. As he said, he was "uncertain how it happened."

If you go to Massachusetts today, you can see the house in Weymouth where Abigail lived as a child; the house in Quincy to which John brought her after they were married; and the house in Quincy where they lived after they came back from Europe and to which they returned after John's Presidency. All of these places are close together and near Boston.

In the Quincy house, you will see many things that Abigail used. The furniture she brought from Europe is still there, although it no longer has the crimson upholstery. Her big four-poster bed is still in the bedroom.

The tiles which John Quincy brought to her from Europe are still around the fireplace in her room. A box hedge that was in the garden when Abigail came to the house is still growing, as well as a rosebush she planted from clippings she brought from Europe.

If you go to the White House in Washington, you will see the beautiful East Room as it is today. Perhaps you will remember that it is the same room in which Abigail Adams had the laundry hung when she was the President's Lady.

REGINA Z. KELLY

PIPER BOOKS

ABIGAIL ADAMS: *The President's Lady,* by Regina Z. Kelly
JOHN ALDEN: *Steadfast Pilgrim,* by Cecile Pepin Edwards
ETHAN ALLEN: *Green Mountain Hero,* by Sheldon N. Ripley
HANS CHRISTIAN ANDERSEN: *Fairy Tale Author,* by Shannon Garst
DAN BEARD: *Boy Scout Pioneer,* by Jerry Seibert
DANIEL BOONE: *Wilderness Trailblazer,* by Miriam E. Mason
KIT CARSON: *Mountain Scout,* by Donald E. Worcester
HENRY CLAY: *Statesman and Patriot,* by Regina Z. Kelly
CHRISTOPHER COLUMBUS: *Sailor and Dreamer,* by Bernadine Bailey
AMELIA EARHART: *First Lady of the Air,* by Jerry Seibert
HENRY FORD: *Maker of the Model T,* by Miriam Gilbert
BENJAMIN FRANKLIN: *First Great American,* by John Tottle
ULYSSES S. GRANT: *General and President,* by Joseph Olgin
JOHN HANCOCK: *Friend of Freedom,* by Jeannette C. Nolan
PATRICK HENRY: *Voice of Liberty,* by William Percival Jones
MATTHEW HENSON: *Arctic Hero,* by Sheldon N. Ripley
SAM HOUSTON: *Friend of the Indians,* by Joseph Olgin
HENRY HUDSON: *Explorer of the North,* by Dorothea J. Snow
THOMAS JEFFERSON: *Champion of the People,* by Joseph Olgin
JOHN PAUL JONES: *Soldier of the Sea,* by Donald E. Worcester
ABRAHAM LINCOLN: *Man of Courage,* by Bernadine Bailey
JAMES MADISON: *Statesman and President,* by Regina Z. Kelly
FERDINAND MAGELLAN: *Noble Captain,* by Katharine Wilkie
HORACE MANN: *Sower of Learning,* by Cecile Pepin Edwards
KING PHILIP: *Loyal Indian,* by Cecile Pepin Edwards
JUAN PONCE DE LEON: *First in the Land,* by Bernadine Bailey
PONTIAC: *Lion in the Forest,* by Wilma Pitchford Hays
JOHN WESLEY POWELL: *Canyon's Conqueror,* by Marian T. Place
PAUL REVERE: *Colonial Craftsman,* by Regina Z. Kelly
SACAJAWEA: *Guide to Lewis and Clark,* by Jerry Seibert
JOHN SMITH: *Man of Adventure,* by Miriam E. Mason
ROBERT LOUIS STEVENSON: *Storyteller and Adventurer,*
     by Katharine Wilkie
HARRIET TUBMAN: *Flame of Freedom,* by Frances T. Humphreville